THE INVENTORS

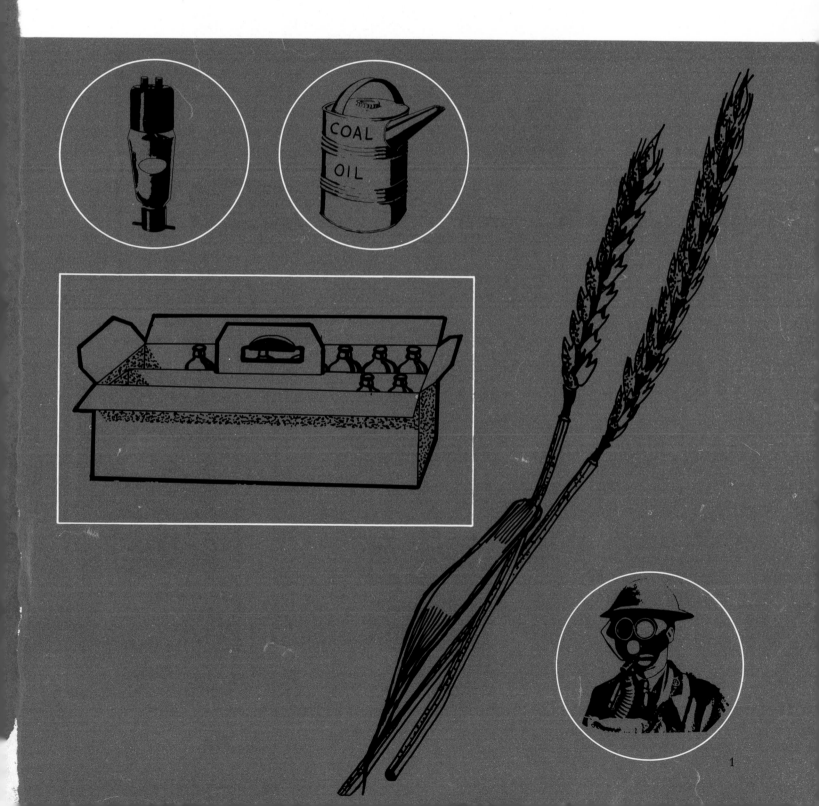

1

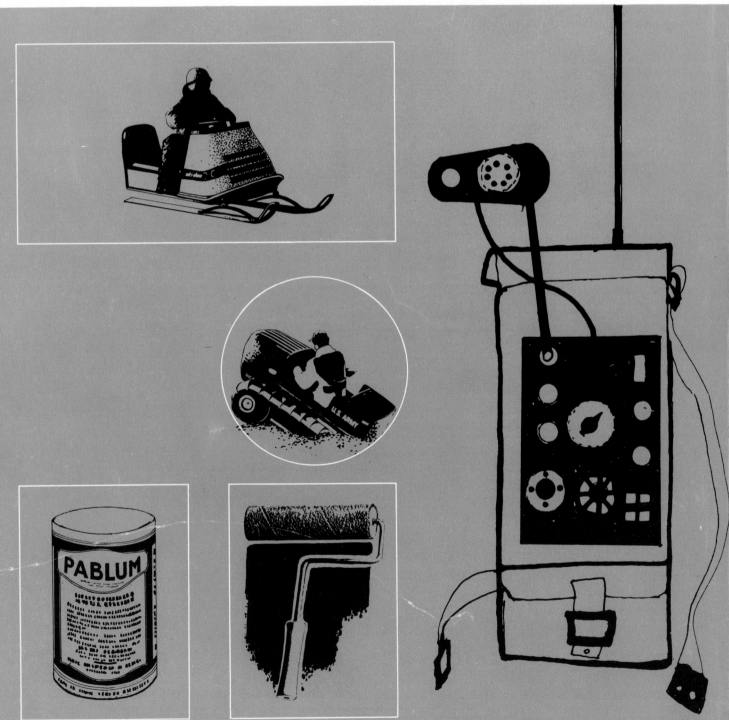

THE INVENTORS
GREAT IDEAS IN CANADIAN ENTERPRISE

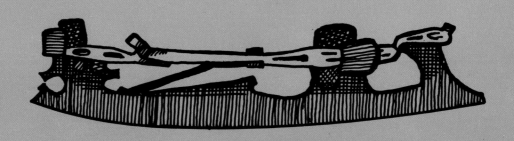

BY J.J.BROWN

The Canadian Illustrated Library

THE CANADIAN ILLUSTRATED LIBRARY
McCLELLAND AND STEWART LIMITED,

ILLUSTRATED BOOKS DIVISION

150 Simcoe Street, Toronto 1, Ont., Canada.

PUBLISHER: JACK McCLELLAND
EDITORIAL DIRECTOR: PIERRE BERTON
CREATIVE DIRECTOR: FRANK NEWFELD
EDITOR: LESLIE F. HANNON
ART DIRECTOR: KEITH SCOTT
ASSIST. ART DIRECTOR: HUGH MICHAELSON
STAFF DESIGNER: NICK MILTON
ASSISTANT EDITOR: WALT McDAYTER
EXECUTIVE ASSISTANT: ENNIS HALLIDAY

CONTENTS

AN INTRODUCTION
BY PIERRE BERTON

The missing chapter
in our history

In 1960 when J. J. Brown first set about trying to raise money to support massive and original research on the subject of Canadian invention and technology, all the company and university presidents he talked to told him it was a crazy scheme. There *were* no Canadian inventors, they insisted. But Brown, who was convinced that this constituted a missing chapter in the history of Canada, kept on. He talked personally to thirty-nine top executives. No luck. He wrote to two hundred more. They turned him down.

He was about to give up when he encountered Thomas Eadie and the picture changed. Without the help of Eadie and his firm – the Bell Telephone Company – this book would not exist today. This enlightened attitude is perhaps understandable since the Bell company bears the name of the greatest Canadian inventor of them all. Yet Alexander Graham Bell is only one inventor out of thousands, some of whose discoveries have made major industries possible (such as the oil industry and the air transport industry). Since the Patent Office at Ottawa opened in 1824, Canadian nationals alone have filed plans for a staggering number of devices – estimated at 200,000; and new ones keep pouring in from all sources at the rate of four hundred every month.

Many of these inventions are frivolous, nutty or impractical. (Did you know, for instance, that there are one hundred variations on the can opener registered every year in Canada alone?) But, in his exhaustive coast-to-coast research, Dr. Brown has unearthed close to four thousand which he considered to be *bona fide* contributions to world technology. The most significant and interesting are detailed in this volume.

This is a tightly written book. It has to be because there is so much to say. Its prose is sparse: you can't glamorize a screw propeller in the way you can an Indian raid . . . though one may be vastly more significant than the other. But there is a surprise on almost every page because, like the industrial and academic leaders who scoffed at the author, Canadians have generally failed to recognize the contribution their countrymen have made to technological history. Until I read Dr. Brown's manuscript, I had no idea that our own inventive genius was primarily responsible for the variable-pitch propeller, the gas mask, the wirephoto, the snow blower, the walkie talkie, the automatic post office, the modern system of newspaper photo-engraving, the coded steam foghorn, the hydrofoil and the electric organ.

In the present book, Dr. Brown has not got space to mention the carbon cigarette filter or the pocket pack of facial tissue, devised – twenty years too soon, alas – by Eric Leaver, of Toronto, whose blind-landing system for aircraft brought him $100,000 when he was a stripling of 18. Nor, for that matter, does the author mention his own invention, the inflatable umbrella – an ingenious device that, like so many others, came to naught.

If there is a lesson in this book it is that Canadians rarely recognize their inventive geniuses and that the vast majority of these geniuses derive little financial gain from their brainchildren: One has only to examine the experience of Toronto's Norman Breakey who devised, in 1940, the first paint roller but was unable to produce it in quantity before others jumped in and adapted it as their own. Archibald Huntsman's discovery of the principle of fast-freezing fish (more than forty years ago) and U. V. Helava's map-making computer shared a similar fate. No Canadian company was interested in gambling on these ideas so that today the u.s. is the world's biggest producer of frozen foods and an Italian firm manufactures the map-maker.

Jack Brown is a tenacious and prolific man. Teacher, editor, financial counsel, management consultant and historian, he is the author of more than one hundred articles in learned, literate, technical and popular journals and of fourteen books, including two best sellers – one on investment and another on insurance. His interest in the present subject dates back to 1942 when at Yale he wrote a prize-winning doctoral dissertation on the effect of technology on society. The main work began in April 1962 when, equipped with four cameras, a tape recorder and a notebook, he set out on the first of four extended coast-to-coast tours of Canada on a research project that had never before been attempted. Altogether, in four years, Brown visited some three hundred communities, talking to anyone who knew anything about inventors or inventions. This book, and a longer, more academic volume, *Ideas in Exile,* are the results.

The significance of Brown's findings is incalculable. Like so much of Canadian history, the story of our technical achievements has largely gone unchronicled. But it must now be obvious from what the author has unearthed that Canadians have made contributions to technology out of all proportion to their small numbers. Perhaps, as the author himself once said, it is because of our long winter evenings; or it may be that we have simply underestimated our own native ingenuity. Self-effacement has long been considered a Canadian trait; inventiveness has not. As the nation enters its second century, this milestone of a book may go a long way toward eliminating the first of our characteristics and illuminating the second.

PROLOGUE
The Struggle for Recognition

The way we live, and the way we earn a living, have been determined by how our fathers treated the inventors of the past. The way our children will live depends on how we treat inventors living today.

By and large, our past treatment of inventors has been contemptible. Not only have we allowed them to be robbed blind by both business and government, and failed to support them with either tax help or grants the way we have done for painters, puppeteers, and poets, but, unlike other nations, we have never even accorded them social recognition, which costs nothing. No Canadian inventor has ever been honoured for his work by the public at large.

Few of us even realize that Canadians have made important contributions to the world's store of scientific and technical information – many of the key discoveries or inventions that produced major industries and, therefore, thousands of jobs. Although Canada is still a "young" country, in the industrial sense, very few of us are aware that many basic industrial ideas (such as drilling for oil) were first tried here. Pioneering work of world significance in telephone and telegraph, postal service, agriculture, building technology, aviation, water transport, geophysics and automation – to name only a few that come readily to mind – has been carried out in Canada.

Wallace Turnbull's variable-pitch propeller was, for instance, the key invention that, by providing the equivalent of a gearshift, made the air transport industry possible. Contra-rotating propellers and inertial navigation were both developed very early here. Canada has played an important role in atomic physics. Lord Rutherford did much of his early work at Montreal's McGill University; we have a well-established radioactive metals industry; we pioneered the development of the heavy-water atomic pile. The world's first hydrofoil boat was operating in Nova Scotia as far back as 1919. The world's first record-controlled machine tool was developed in Toronto, with the basic patent held by two young Canadians. In construction technology, Canadians have contributed in such fields as hard-rock tunnelling, building on muskeg, and concrete work in sub-zero weather.

Great things are usually done by great men. Canadians can feel legitimate pride in the stories of the heroic men who, in spite of heart-breaking difficulties came up with these and a host of other inventions we have all enjoyed. The story of Canadian invention is, for the most part, the story of the struggles of individuals to achieve recognition from an indifferent society.

In a world still concerned with narrow nationalism and where just about everything is expressed in legalistic officialese, we need some definition of what is a "Canadian inventor" and what is, even more simply, an "invention." Professors have written entire books distinguishing between "ideas," "discoveries," "inventions" and "developments," but let us establish that an invention is an idea embodied into a piece of physical equipment which provides some goods or services we didn't have before. Innovation is all the above, but it need not involve physical equipment.

It must be also established and emphasized that there is really no such thing as a genuine single inventor who is uniquely responsible for a particular invention. Every man stands on the shoulders of his predecessors. The number of early partial anticipations of any invention depends only on the amount of money you are willing to spend on research. The whole story of the airplane does not start with Wilbur Wright but with Leonardo da Vinci – and even earlier than that. Thus the turn-of-the-century mythology of the inventor as hero, epitomized by Thomas Alva Edison, depended largely on the combined ignorance of writer and audience.

The definition of a "Canadian inventor" is a little more difficult. The proper history of invention would be one which described how human beings progressively improved their

Author, Dr. J. J. Brown in his Montreal study.

control over their environment. It would pay no attention to whether a particular advance was made by the Chinese, the Americans, Greeks or the Canadians. But the 19th century was a period of intense nationalism in the Western world, and we are still prisoners of the kind of thinking it engendered. Moreover, nationalism is a stage that every growing nation must go through, just as every individual must go through adolescence. Before a history of world technology can be written, each nation must have prepared a nationalist-oriented story of what innovations its own people have produced. This is the lawyer's brief for Canada.

My working definition of a *Canadian* invention has been either that the inventor got his education here, or that the basic concept of the invention came to him while he was living in Canada. There are, of course, borderline cases where another nation has a claim to the paternity of a given invention because the inventor – even a Canadian-born inventor – was living there when it was produced. I have attempted to state the Canadian claim, leaving it to later historians to adjudicate between the claims of several nations, if our descendants think this worth doing.

Medicine has been omitted entirely, partly because it is both art and science (hence technology tells only part of the story) and partly because the rise of pharmacology and chemical methods of treating disease has tended to make large areas of medical instrumentation obsolete.

A second major area I have omitted is world technology applied in Canada. That is, a given technology, such as bridge building, is included only if it led to some Canadian inventions. For example, I treat the development of the railways, mainly a British technology, because it led to a flood of Canadian inventions; I do not treat the technology of road building, bridge building, dwelling construction, microwave links, modern pipelines, or the St. Lawrence Seaway, because they inspired no major Canadian invention.

Next, the question arises, what is an *important* invention? We are amused by the mechanical skirt lifter invented by the Calgary lady in the 1890s to help her get across the muddy streets, but it cannot be considered an important patent from any point of view. The criterion I have tried to use is basically an economic one. How many million dollars' business does that industry now do every year? How many jobs have been created by the new industry? What I have tried to assess is the change that the invention has made in our lives because of its economic impact, as well as the satisfaction of having had something to do with a great new idea.

When we reach the 20th century, the problem of selection becomes critical. The editors of the Oxford University Press's five-volume history of technology explain in their preface that they thought it wise to stop about 1880. The authors felt they couldn't carry their work further partly because modern technology has become increasingly complex and more and more scientific terms are required to describe it, but chiefly because of the difficulty that "lies in the nature of technological history – and perhaps of all history – for this must be based on the selection from an immense number of events of those which have proved most significant for future ages. The choice of such events from the distant past is a very different operation from the semi-prophetic selection of the significant happenings of a recent generation." In the case of a history of Canadian invention and technology, all these risks must be assumed. Until 1900, Canada was basically a pioneer country, and invention can't really get started until the basic pioneer wants for food and shelter and a degree of security have been satisfied. Necessity is, in truth, seldom the mother of invention. Thus, in order to present a reasonable picture of the history of Canadian invention and technology, I have no choice but to bring the story up to the very moment of going to press.

In this painting, the young Alexander Graham Bell holds a model of the human ear, made for him by the family's Brantford doctor in 1874. It led Bell, by many brilliant steps, to the principle of the telephone.

BELL HIS AMAZING INVENTIONS CHANGED THE WHOLE WORLD

The telephone, "the greatest single invention of the age," developed from Alexander Graham Bell's experiments at Brantford, Ontario. His genius also gave mankind the ideas that resulted in film sound tracks, the electric eye, the metal detector, the hydrofoil boat, the iron lung, and many other boons.

Even Montreal's supposedly cynical reporters were impressed as they tested Bell's telephone — at least this illustrator thought so.

During the U.S. centennial celebrations of 1876, Philadelphia staged a world fair, and here Bell created a sensation with his "talking wires." Dom Pedro, Emperor of Brazil, listens with astonishment to Bell (left) reciting "To be or not to be."

Grandpa listens-in to a telephone pole: an early cartoonist lampoons the general incredulity about the telephone.

Strange shapes that soared over Baddeck Bay

It came to be known as Kite Field, that sloping meadow near the Beinn Bhreagh estate at Baddeck, N.S., where much to the amusement and consternation of Cape Bretoners, Alexander Graham Bell filled the sky with the strange giant kites that represented, for Canada, the beginning of aviation. The kites came in weird and wondrous forms, some star-shaped, others round or square, while one resembled a flying paddlewheel. Bell was 54 years old and grey-bearded in 1901 when he perfected the triangular-celled structures that he used for his "tetrahedral" kites, but he still had the dynamic drive to tug the line of his gliding machines with men far younger than he. His first tetrahedral model contained only 16 winged cells, and whistled like a Banshee in the Maritime wind, but in 1902 it flew well enough to convince Bell to build bigger ones – the Victor, White Flyer, Oionos, Aerodrome, *and in 1905, the* Frostking, *which lifted a man 30 feet into the air. In 1907 Bell founded the Aerial Experiment Association, and one of its members – Thomas Selfridge — on December 6 of that year became the first man to perform a sustained flight on a tetrahedral kite, the* Cygnet I, *which flew 168 feet high for seven minutes – before it crashed and was wrecked in the cold waters of the Bras d'Or Lakes. Miraculously, Selfridge escaped uninjured. From kites, the A.E.A. moved to engine-equipped airplanes, beginning with the* Redwing, *then on to the* Whitewing, June Bug, *and finally, the most famous of them all – the* Silver Dart, *which above the ice-covered surface of the lake at Baddeck, on February 23, 1909 became the first heavier-than-air machine to fly in the British Commonwealth.*

The huge kite Cygnet II *weighed 950 pounds and contained 3,690 cells. Equipped in 1909 with the* Silver Dart *engine, it proved too heavy to fly.*

Some kites were small, handled by one man; others were towed by horse, launch, even by steamboat.

The steerable "tricycle" landing gear of the early aircraft developed by Bell and his associates represented a genuine world first for Canada.

The Silver Dart, *piloted by J. A. D. McCurdy, as it took off from the frozen surface of Bras d'Or Lakes on the first powered flight in Canada. It travelled about half a mile, at a height varying from 10 to 30 feet, and at about 40 miles an hour.*

The rich legacy of Bell's creative mind

To remember Bell only as the inventor of the telephone is to seriously underrate his creative genius. He was the Leonard da Vinci of the modern age, with a restless curiosity that probed into many fields. Son of a professor of vocal physiology, he first found fame in voice mechanics, teaching the deaf to speak, and contributed to the teaching method called "visible speech," introduced by his father. In aviation, besides developing the first airplane to fly in Canada, he led experiments with rockets and helicopter blades. In navigation, he gave the world its first successful hydrofoil craft. His photophone, which transmitted speech by light rays, was the first step towards film sound track. The versatile Bell even went in for sheep-raising, developing a breed that tended to give birth to twins and triplets.

Bell's solar still, for making salt water drinkable.

Bell's device to detect a bullet inside a body (see below).

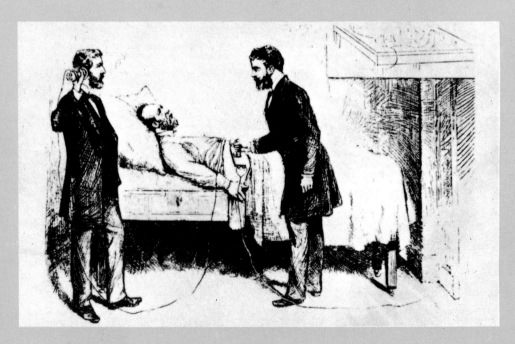

At the deathbed of James A. Garfield, Bell (left) *made a desperate bid with a sound-wave probe to detect the bullet that was killing the U.S. President . . . to no avail. Garfield was shot in Washington on July 2, 1881, and after lingering between life and death for two months, he died of blood poisoning. Later models of Bell's metal detector received wide use and good results before the advent of X-Rays.*

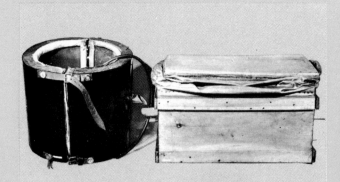

A vacuum jacket, later adapted to easy-childbirth techniques.

Tetrahedral-structured, this Bell museum is at Baddeck, N.S.

A rocket model, used by Bell to study jet propulsion in 1893.

A scale model of "The Cigar" – Bell's HD4 hydrofoil craft.

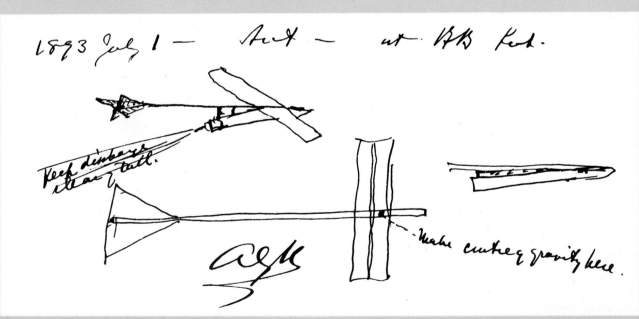

Ten years before the Wright brothers flew at Kitty Hawk, Bell recorded this experiment with rocket-powered model airplanes.

1 / TRANSPORTATION

Better ways to get there

Sometimes science and technology seem far removed from everyday life and we want to leave such difficult matters to the scientists. When tempted, we should consider this: if the automatic exchange hadn't been invented, and we still needed people to plug in connections, just about every woman in the u.s. over 18 would have to be a telephone girl!

Invention is never closer to us in our fast-moving world than it is in the field of transportation. As seen on a graph, the curve of speeds remained almost horizontal for thousands of years before 1900; men walked at three miles an hour, rode the pony express at nearly 20, and, finally, the crack express train hit 100. Then, suddenly, the curve on the graph began to look like the vapour trail of a jet fighter zooming up. With fast cars, aircraft and finally rockets, the curve climbed almost vertically to 200, then 400 and now to 4,000 miles an hour.

Canadians have played a role in the transportation story out of all proportion to their small numbers. The fastest clipper ships were designed and built by the McKay brothers of Nova Scotia; the first ship to cross the Atlantic entirely under steam was built in Quebec; the first successful hydrofoil came from Baddeck.

Only one major Canadian inventor ended his life in the poorhouse. He was John Patch, a native of Yarmouth, Nova Scotia, who has a strong claim to the invention of the screw propeller. This is a key advance that made modern ocean navigation possible. Steam was not a serious competitor to sail so long as the power had to be applied to the water through awkward, space-consuming, and inefficient paddle wheels. It was only toward the middle of the 19th century, when screw propellers were developed, that marine steam power came into its own. Like many important inventions, the screw propeller has several fathers in different countries. Canada's claim, through John Patch, although well documented, is little known.

My chief source of information about Patch and his invention is a petition made to the Nova Scotia Legislature on his behalf in 1858, a quarter of a century after he had demonstrated the propeller in Yarmouth Harbour. By this time Patch was an old man, crippled and destitute.

Some time before 1833, he had conceived the idea of propelling ships the way a small boat is sculled by moving a single oar in a particular pattern over its stern. In 1833 a crude wooden model of the machine, consisting apparently of a screw propeller turned by a hand-crank to which it was joined by wooden gears, was first tried out at Yarmouth. The first trials were done at night, but later, in the summer of 1833, the hand-propelled boat was seen by many witnesses making its way around the harbour without benefit of wind.

The great screw propellers of the giant ships of the sea – like this 35-ton specimen from the Cunarder Queen Mary *– owe their origin to a hand-cranked version built with wooden gears by Nova Scotian John Patch in 1833.*

Old-timers in Yarmouth claim they remember a story that R. D. Butler and his brother Nathan helped Patch make the machinery. It looked like a windlass, and was turned by two men standing on deck. One man claims he remembers seeing some bits and pieces of the device when he was a child but, since it was made of wood, it is unlikely that any trace remains.

The next trial probably took place a year later. By this time Patch had installed his system for propulsion in a good-sized boat, the schooner *Royal George*, Captain Silas C. Kelley. Kelley told of being with Patch on board the boat in the summer of 1834 or 1835. Becalmed with many other craft some distance below the harbour of Saint John, the two men, turning the machinery by means of a crank, got the *Royal George* moving and soon left all the other vessels behind.

The basic idea of the screw propeller was stirring in many minds in the first 30 years of the 19th century. By 1833, when Patch had his invention working, all the major types of screw propellers had been suggested, at least in the patent literature. On the other hand, not very much of real practical value had been accomplished. Two or three ships had been driven for a brief period by screw propellers of various types, but the paddle wheel was still the undisputed method of driving large boats. It was not until 1836 that Francis Smith, with the help of a wealthy and perceptive London banker, put together a screw propeller that really worked. This was in the *Archimedes* (3,700 tons), the first screw steamer

built in London. The British did not try screw propulsion for their navy until the 1840s.

It seems probable that the Canadian John Patch was working in the forefront of the development of the screw propeller. Overcoming handicaps that would have stopped any ordinary man – such as the lack of education, or access to technical literature — he made a vital contribution to marine transport.

Patch was probably a seaman or a fisherman. Born in 1789, he was probably married in 1804, had a first child, a girl, in 1805, and died in 1861. R. B. Blauveldt, the Yarmouth historian, believes that the petition to the Nova Scotia Legislature was written by C. B. Owen, a brilliant lawyer and great orator of the period. Certainly the petition and the accompanying letters were written by an unusual man. The plea ends: ". . . he conceives he has rendered essential service to the world at large, and although other men may make their fortunes by his invention and the commercial world be benefitted by it, he would simply ask for the necessary means to enable him to support himself comfortably and respectably . . . We can see the Honourable The House of Nova Scotia would do an act worthy of itself in appropriating a sum to reward the mechanical genius of one of its own sons in the person of Mr. Patch."

The petition failed. The legislature in its session of 1858 passed a private act to incorporate the Nova Scotia Barristers' Society, another to incorporate the North British Society, and a third to incorporate the Trustees of the Baptist Church of Falmouth, but

the appeal of a man who probably invented one of the major marine devices of modern times went entirely unheeded.

McPherson's disposable ship

Canada's claim to shipbuilding fame rests on the surprising, not to say fantastic, idea of the disposable ship. The building of wooden ships is an ancient craft in every part of the world, so it is unlikely to find a genuine technical innovation in a country that is a relative newcomer to the art. Our 18th and 19th century wooden sailing ships were essentially similar to those being built in other parts of the world. But the basic idea of the disposable ship seems to be completely new.

In the early 1820s the British government put a timber tax on oak and squared pine. This was a basic export of Lower Canada, and the tax immediately crippled a thriving trade. In 1824 a man named McPherson came up with the idea that a ship could be built entirely of squared timbers temporarily pegged together, sailed across the ocean, and then dismantled in Britain. This would effectively get around the British timber tax, because there was no law against dismantling a ship and using its timber for other purposes. Accordingly, towards the middle of 1824, the *Columbus* slid down the ways at Quebec City. She was a huge timber drogher, displacing 3,690 tons.

Although she couldn't have been easy to handle, the ship made the voyage to England safely. Then, for some obscure reason, she was not broken up as planned. She made a

The Accommodation,
*built by John Molson
in 1809, was Canada's
first steamship.*

return trip to Quebec City and then turned around and once more headed for the United Kingdom. On her second voyage she ran into a storm and was lost with all hands.

In the meantime (that is, probably late in 1824), a second timber drogher of the disposable type was built in the Quebec City yards. This ship was 304 feet long and displaced the tremendous total of 5,294 tons, the largest in the world until the building of the *Great Republic* a generation later. While specific information on the fate of this second disposable ship is hard to come by, it looks as if she made a successful voyage to England and was there broken up for the timber. However, soon after this, the British tax laws were changed again and the idea languished.

Molson's amazing steamship

The first steamship built entirely in North America was built in Canada rather than in the United States. This is so astonishing that, even now, it is difficult to see reasons why a device representing the highest technology of its day should be built in an impoverished colony, rather than in the commercial and industrial centre of the continent. Historian Merrill Denison says: "For its time and place, Molson's achievement was as incredible as if someone today were to build a jet-engined plane on the east shore of Hudson Bay and fly it successfully to Churchill."

It took a bold man to argue the practicality of steamships in the first decade of the 19th century. In 1787 John Fitch actually demonstrated a steamboat to American Congressmen,

but Fitch committed suicide, destitute and a drunkard, in 1798. Robert Fulton achieved the first successful operation of a steam vessel in 1807, when he ran his *Clermont* from New York to Albany and back, in spite of grave prognostications from the authorities. Fulton died scorned and neglected in 1815 but, soon afterwards, a successful commercial service was operating on the Hudson and other inland rivers of the United States. Without denigrating Fulton's accomplishments, it should be said that the engines for his boat were built, not in America, but by Boulton & Watt in England. Since the British at that time had a policy of refusing export permits for mechanical devices, the fact that Fulton got his engine is a tribute to his diplomatic ability and perseverance. But the *Clermont* is not really an example of American engineering.

John Molson, the man who did build North America's first domestic steamship, was born in England in 1763. A hearty six-footer with engaging ways, he also possessed a keen eye for business. At the age of 19 he came to Canada and set up in Montreal the brewery which still bears the family name. By the turn of the century, he had become a leading Montreal capitalist.

Molson probably got his idea for a steamboat on the St. Lawrence from the Winans Brothers, of Burlington, Vermont. Early in 1808 the Winans began construction of a steamboat in Vermont which, by the end of that year, was operating on Lake Champlain powered by an English engine. Molson may even have made a trip up the Richelieu and visited Burling-

Samuel Cunard, of Halifax, was a principal shareholder of the Royal William (left), which in 1833 became the first ship to cross the Atlantic entirely on steam.

Below, an artist's conception of the wooden paddlewheeler as she was being built at Wolfe's Cove, Quebec, in 1830. The Royal William spanned 182 feet, weighed 1,370 tons gross and had a speed of about eight knots. She was eventually sold to Spain, and became one of the world's first steam-powered warships.

ton in the summer of 1808 to see the boat, since he sold beer in that entire district.

A cash book unearthed by Denison among the papers at the Molson brewery, and a contract turned up by the curator of the Provincial Judicial Archives for the District of Montreal, prove conclusively that Molson's steamboat, the *Accommodation*, was designed and built of Canadian materials in Montreal. The contract, dated June 5, 1809, sets up a partnership between John Molson, John Jackson, an engineer, and John Bruce, a shipbuilder. The three Johns were to build a steamship for service on the St. Lawrence and share equally in the profits. The cash book shows that work had begun on April 1 of that year and proves further that the heavy castings for the engine itself were built at the Forges St. Maurice, at Three Rivers, Quebec. No engineering details have survived, but the boat was launched successfully on August 19 at a total cost of nearly 2,000 pounds sterling – an immense sum in those days.

On November 6, 1809, the *Accommodation*, with ten paying passengers, arrived at Quebec City from Montreal. The contemporary account in the Quebec *Mercury* describes her as being driven by two side paddlewheels, with a length of 85 feet on deck, and 75 at the waterline. The report says, "No wind or tide can stop her," but the story in the other Quebec paper, the *Gazette*, gives a somewhat different picture:

"On Sunday last she went up against wind and tide from Brahaut's Wharf to Lymburner's, but her progress was very slow. It is obvious that

With enough sails for a flotilla, giant timber rafts made their way down the St. Lawrence.

The square timber rafts were travelling communities on which men worked, slept and ate.

20

Most serviceable of all early Canadian river craft was the Durham boat, designed for shallow waterways. Built with a rounded bow, it was steered by a long rudder and propelled by sail or pushed by poles.

her machinery at present has not sufficient force for this river, but there can be no doubt of the possibility of perfectionating it so as to answer every purpose for which it is intended."

The *Accommodation* had taken 36 hours to make the trip from Montreal to Quebec City. This seems slow to us today but 150 years ago travellers often took a week for that journey, whether they went by boat or coach. This was the first voyage of the first steamboat in Canada, and the first steamboat in North America to be built locally of local materials.

Nothing whatsoever remains of the *Accommodation*. Canada's first major technological triumph has disappeared so completely that, if it were not for the written record of her building costs, the story of her construction might be dismissed as a figment of imagination. At one time it was thought that the pulpit of a church at Ste. Adèle, Quebec, was made from the oak salvaged from the deckhouse but even this is uncertain. It is true that the pulpit was made from old oak timbers found in the basement of one of the Molson breweries, but the connection between this stock of timber and the *Accommodation* is tenuous.

By steamer to England

The first vessel to make the west-east passage of the Atlantic entirely under steam was the Canadian paddlewheeler *Royal William*, built at Quebec by Black & Campbell in the winter of 1830-31. Bennett & Henderson, of Montreal, built the side-lever engines of 200 h.p.

The original plan for the *Royal William* was to have her sail between Quebec and Halifax. In 1831 she made several trips down the river to the Maritimes, but the next year no trips were possible because of a cholera epidemic, and it was said that the owners lost 16,000 pounds sterling in the venture.

When she left Pictou for England on August 18, 1833, the *Royal William* had seven passengers, but her chief cargo was 324 tons of coal. On September 6, she put in to the harbour at Cowes, Isle of Wight, after a run of some twenty days. Most of the crossing was made under steam, except for the intervals when the engines had to be turned off and the fires extinguished so the boilers could be cleaned. This scraping of salt out of the boilers had to take place every fourth day and required 24 hours.

While the *Royal William* was not a financial success and was eventually sold to the Spanish Navy, her voyage marks the beginning of the great era of North Atlantic steam navigation. Samuel Cunard, of Halifax, who was an early investor in the ship, went on to found his great North Atlantic steamship line.

The river freighters

As canals with locks replaced the laborious hand-carry of the portages around Canada's many rapids, it was possible to make freight boats larger and heavier. The *voyageur's* birchbark canoe itself was surprisingly large, capable of carrying twelve men and half a ton of freight. A beautiful specimen can be seen in the National Museum at Ottawa. But it

was fragile and easily pierced by rocks. The *batteau*, the next development, was a large flat-bottomed boat with straight sides. *Batteaux* could carry 20 to 24 barrels of flour as cargo, and were strong enough to withstand repeated collisions with reefs, but they were far too heavy to be carried over portages. By 1800, the Durham boat, developed on Lake Ontario, had pretty well taken over the heavy carrying trade of the St. Lawrence. Capable of carrying 100 barrels to the *batteau's* 24, it was large enough to run the Lachine Rapids outside Montreal.

Very soon after the British conquest, a demand for square timbers opened up in England. Trees were available in abundance along the north shore of Lake Ontario and the only requirement was a method of transporting the logs to Quebec City for loading on ships. The logs were trimmed into square sections with an adze and then assembled into enormous rafts. These were large enough to carry many men as well as a large deckload of staves, deals (that is, lumber cut to a specified size), and barrels of wheat and potash.

Built on the ice during the winter, the rafts floated down the rivers and lakes at spring breakup, guided by large oars, and sometimes, if the wind was favourable, by crude sails. As early as 1790, a timber raft from the Bay of Quinte on Lake Ontario reached Quebec City. Philemon Wright, a Loyalist who had set up a large lumbering establishment near Hull, was making regular shipments by raft in 1806. From this beginning, Hull became one of Canada's leading lumber, pulp and paper centres.

Alexander Graham Bell, at 27

Flying on water

Alexander Graham Bell was probably the first person to realize the full potential of the boat that climbs out of the water at speed and runs supported by hydrofoils, or small wings. The wings sustain the boat by acting on the water just the way the larger wings of aircraft act on air. Back as far as 1903, when Bell was experimenting with his giant kites, he needed a fast method of towing experimental kites over the water.

Speed on water is a difficult problem. The resistance of the water to the passage of the boat increases with the amount of wetted surface – the larger the hull, the slower the speed. What is worse, the resistance of the water is not a linear function but increases with the cube of the boat's speed. For example, when the speed rises from five to ten miles an hour the resistance does not double, but increases eight times. Bell and F. W. "Casey" Baldwin, working together, first experimented on models then, by 1907, actually had a hydrofoil craft working on Baddeck Bay, Cape Breton Island.

The basic idea of using "water wings" to lift a boat off the water was not new. There is a well-authenticated record of a towed hydrofoil boat being tested in England as early as 1861, and in 1897 the Count de Lambert had a steampowered boat on hydroplanes. By 1907 the idea had been tested in England by Meachan, in France by Santos Dumont, in the United States by Cooper-Hewitt, and in Italy by Ricaldi and Forlanini.

Nevertheless, the first really successful hydrofoil craft was developed by Baldwin and Bell in the summer of 1908. Twenty feet long and weighing less than 400 pounds, the boat was towed at eight miles an hour to test the action of the hydrofoils. With Baldwin and 145 pounds of lead aboard to represent the engine weight, she rose out of the water as if by magic. When a workman on the tow craft saw the pull on the tow rope drop to less than eleven pounds, he ejaculated in Gaelic: "*Dhonnas Beag (the little devil)!*" Baldwin felt this wasn't a bad description of the boat, and from that time on *Dhonnas Beag* was its name.

During the summer there were many heartbreaking failures, and the boat changed its shape almost every day, but on October 20, *Dhonnas Beag* lifted twelve inches clear of the water under power and achieved pure hydrofoil action.

It is remarkable that Bell and Baldwin, in almost their first attempt at designing a hydrofoil boat, came up with the basic configuration used today. The earliest Italian hydrofoils, for example that of Forlanini, were of venetian blind type, a series of curved blades extending below the boat, fore and aft. The *Dhonnas Beag* was equipped with what Baldwin called "reefing hydrocurves." As the craft lifted clear of the water with increasing speed, the upper, larger surfaces would emerge from the water first, decreasing wetted area and therefore water resistance.

By the late fall of 1908, Bell and Baldwin had proved that a hydrofoil driven by air propellers was a highly efficient means of transport. The experiments, however, also proved that the hydrofoil boat, like the airplane, awaited the birth of efficient power plants. The engines available at that time were hopelessly bulky and heavy in relation to their power output. Even with contra-rotating propellers, a highly efficient method of transmitting power then relatively unknown, the engine of the *Dhonnas Beag* could not keep her off the water for any length of time.

It was not until 1911 that, encouraged by what seemed to be considerable improvement in aircraft engines, Bell and Baldwin got to work once more on the hydrofoil project. Beginning as before with models, in the summers of 1912 through 1914 they tested a fantastic variety of hydrofoils and similar craft. Bell was convinced that hydrofoils could be applied even to sailing boats, a feat only recently achieved.

The outbreak of World War I interrupted the experiments as Bell, then living in Washington, doubted the propriety of an American citizen carrying on experiments which might have military significance in Canada, which was already at war. But when the United States entered the war in 1917, Bell was even more convinced of the military value of hydrofoils and the experiments began again.

Immediately, Bell rushed to Nova Scotia and conferred with Baldwin about hydrofoil submarine chasers. In the summer of 1912, Baldwin had got the first hydrodrome, the H.D. 1, up to 45 miles an hour, hence he and Bell were the world authorities on the subject.

The H.D. 4, built in a crash programme the summer of 1917, embodied everything they had learned in previous hydrofoil boats. It was

Bell's H.D. 4 in 1919 became the fastest boat in the world when it was clocked skimming the water's surface at 70.86 miles an hour.

Principles of the hydrofoil, pioneered by Bell, helped make possible the design of the R.C.N.'s 151-foot-long aluminum craft, Bras d'Or.

For snow-clear rails and a tidier track, one company advertised the merits of installing a broom behind the snowplow.

larger than any of its predecessors. A cigar-shaped hull supported on three sets of reefing hydrofoils was to be driven by airplane propellers powered by two 400 h.p. Liberty engines. After many delays, the u.s. Navy was unable to deliver the engines as promised, and twelve-cylinder Renaults of 250 h.p. each were substituted. But even these were not delivered until the summer of 1918. Using these engines, the h.d. 4 reached a top speed of nearly 54 miles an hour in tests in December 1918. During these tests ice was already forming on Baddeck Bay, and the hydrofoil was seen to cut through sheet ice half an inch thick.

Reports made to the u.s. Navy and the Royal Canadian Navy early in 1919 aroused enough interest that the two long-awaited Liberty engines were finally released. With Baldwin at the controls in the late summer of 1919, the h.d. 4 reached the world record speed of 70.86 miles an hour. There was world-wide publicity for this then-fantastic speed, but Baldwin kept his faith, expressed as far back as 1910, that some day speeds of over 100 m.p.h. on water would be commonplace. The record stood until the 1930s, when fast hydroplanes were developed for the Harmsworth Trophy Races at Detroit.

After World War I, government support for hydrofoils was abruptly withdrawn and Bell gradually lost interest. But the Italians and Russians went ahead rapidly between the wars. After 1945 there was a commercial service on hydrofoils between Naples and Sicily, and the Russians began a hydrofoil service on the Volga river.

That Bell and Baldwin were right in their assessment of the hydrofoil is proven by the fact that all navies of the world are now tremendously interested in hydrofoils once more. The u.s. Navy is spending millions of dollars on development, and has designs for hydrofoils over 300 feet in length. Even the Royal Canadian Navy has shown a revived interest in this branch of science, which had its start in Canada. In 1957 the *Bras d'Or*, a 59-foot hydrofoil craft weighing 17½ tons and driven by two Rolls-Royce engines, was launched and tested by the Canadian Navy.

Canada is now engaged in a $10-million hydrofoil research programme, and a new craft, embodying radically new principles, is being built by De Havilland Aircraft of Canada and Marine Industries Ltd., of Sorel.

Getting the trains through

The world railway industry is indebted to a forgotten Toronto dentist, an unemployed inventor and two partners in a small-town machine shop, for the device that made mountain operations possible. Together they developed the rotary snowplow. Soon afterwards, it was being used by railways as far apart as those in the Andes and Siberia, and by all u.s. railways in the north.

The wedge snowplow, which is a simple outgrowth of the cow catcher, dates back to the early days of railroading. But for deep snow and avalanches, it has serious drawbacks. While much faster than a rotary snowplow, its very speed exposes it to dangers. It usually jumps the track if it runs into a wind-packed drift or

a slide containing rocks and trees. The rotary plow is the only safe method of digging out after an avalanche, or clearing a way through the 20-foot deep drifts common in mountain cuts.

The locomotive equipped with a rotary snowplow seems to have been another of those inventions which, though badly needed by an industry, had to come from outside. The basic patent on the device was taken out by J. W. Elliott, a Toronto dentist, in 1869. He called his device a "compound revolving snow shovel" and in essence it is not only the rotary snowplow used by the railways, but the snowblower many householders use today. There was a wheel driven by a rotary engine on a shaft in line with the tracks. Flat plates attached to the rim of the wheel caught the snow and threw it out through an opening in the top of the wheel housing. A shaped steel casing at the forward end of the wheel collected the snow off the tracks and sent it into the revolving jaws of the snowthrower. Elliott tried to get the railways interested, failed, and went back in disgust to dentistry.

Some years later, however, a man called Orange Jull developed the invention by introducing a cutting knife, or cutting wheel, in front of the throwing wheel. About 1880 Jull persuaded the Leslie brothers, of Orangeville, Ontario, to build a full-size working model.

In the winter of 1883-84, the device was mounted on the end of a flat car at the c.p.r. shops in Toronto and tested on a bank of snow and ice especially shovelled into a cut for the occasion. The test was a success, with chunks of snow and ice being thrown as far as 200 feet, but some minor changes were required. First of all, a flanger was needed to keep the device from being derailed in hard snow, and to leave the rails completely free of obstruction after the plow had passed. Moreover, it was found desirable to have a device that would throw the snow to either side of the track, depending on the local terrain.

Leslie Brothers built a new model with a reversible knife, and they also devised a flanger or ice cutter. This new design was taken to the Cook Locomotive Works, in Paterson, New Jersey, for construction, and was operated on the Chicago and North Western Railway in northern Iowa in the winter of 1895-6.

Under actual operating conditions, it was found that the Leslie Brothers' idea of having two contra-rotating wheels required too much power when the snow clogged between them. Back on the drawing board in Orangeville, they produced the single-wheel plow with vanes which automatically reversed their angle when the direction of wheel rotation was changed. This much simpler model passed all tests in Iowa that same winter, even though it had been hastily thrown together. At the Paterson shops, in the summer of 1886, a new production version was built. At trials on the Oregon Short-line division of the Union Pacific it was such a success that the railway bought the plow on the spot, and ordered three more. After this, the rotary snowplow became standard equipment on u.s. railroads.

In 1888 the c.p.r. built eight of the

A wedge snowplow, vintage 1875: effective, but it jumped the track if it hit packed drifts.

Avalanches would have made mountain routes impassible but for the rotary snowplow.

25

Bombardier: snowmobile's inventor

Elliott-Jull snowplows in their Montreal shops. These were larger than any rotary snowplow previously built. No. 101 had a plow wheel nearly ten feet in diameter attached to a solid main shaft eight and a-half inches in diameter turning in a bearing 34 inches long. But even this BSH (battleship) construction proved inadequate for some snow conditions in the Rockies. The plow worked perfectly in the east where snow tended to be dry, but when used on the West Coast on packed wet snow, the snow-throwing flanges tended to fail. To overcome this difficulty, Leslie Brothers came up with a scoop wheel, a great improvement over the old square fan type. With the increase in wheel diameter to eleven feet, and the addition of cut wideners to the sides of the casing, the rotary snowplow became essentially the device we know today.

About 1908 a controversy over the rotary plow developed between the Leslie Brothers and their chief customer in Canada, the C.P.R. The eventual result was a much improved model. During the hard winter of 1908-09, George Bury, who was then general manager of the western lines of the C.P.R., spent what he thought was too much of his time repairing Leslie Brothers' snowplow.

Leslie charged that his brainchild was abused by C.P.R. operators, which was hard to deny. Because there was so much pressure to get the railway in operation again after an avalanche, the standard method of using the rotary plow in the mountains was to put two powerful locomotives behind it and run it into the drift at ten miles an hour. Since avalanches usu-

ally contain not only snow, but large trees, rocks and other debris, the brute force method often seriously damaged the plows.

Bury determined to build a plow that would stop at nothing, and issued instruction that, as a start, the cutting knives were to be made of two-inch armour plate! To build the rest of the plow in proportion would have made the whole locomotive far too heavy, but the device when completed was massive enough. The new C.P.R. snowplow had a wheel which, instead of being built up from steel sheets, was a massive casting with cutter blades attached by hinges to its outer edges. Some idea of its size can be obtained from the fact that the hinge pins themselves were two and a-half inches in diameter. The completed wheel weighed twelve tons, and had to be delicately balanced because of its high running speed.

The first plow completed at Montreal Locomotive Works in January 1911 quickly made a name for itself by running through a 250-yard drift of hard-packed snow without slowing down. The plows have been seen to cut through trees four inches in diameter, and are probably capable of cutting through any obstacle up to the size required to derail the locomotive itself. Rotary plows of this design are still in use today.

Vehicles that go anywhere

After some interesting bouncing about in the early years, the Canadian automobile industry settled down to being a pale copy of the United States'. For some reason, Can-

ada has never even developed cars suited to its climate. Sweden, a much smaller country, much less endowed with resources, has developed at least two outstanding automobiles – the Saab and the Volvo – both well designed for the difficult Swedish climate. And both of these have enjoyed a good sale abroad, including Canada. The rigours of the Canadian climate would seem to demand a small, manoeuvrable, well-heated automobile driven by an air-cooled engine. Since 1907 Canadian automobile manufacturers have provided large, heavy, slow-steering vehicles driven by water-cooled engines. These appear to be designed – if they are designed at all – for use at Palm Springs, California.

With off-road vehicles, the story is different. Since much of Canada has no roads at all, it is not surprising that we have spent a great deal of time and money developing vehicles which can go anywhere. Perhaps the first approach to the off-road vehicle was the caterpillar track. This was described by Leonardo da Vinci, and patented in 1770, but was almost unused until the end of the 19th century. A caterpillar track wagon, pulled by two horses, was in use in Richmond, Quebec, in 1903.

The pioneer developer of the off-road vehicle was Armand Bombardier, of Valcourt, Quebec. He developed his "snowmobile" in 1926, and his vehicles are to be seen wherever heavy loads have to be carried over difficult terrain. The Bombardier muskeg tractor is a vehicle with special wide tracks to keep it from sinking into the muskeg of the far north.

In the Fifties, Bombardier pioneer-

The Sanivan *made garbage collecting quicker and more hygienic.*

ed in the development of small light snow vehicles for winter sports. Vehicles like the *Ski-doo* have caught on, and building light vehicles for towing skiers and for easy cross-country travel in winter has become a big industry in Quebec. They are not an unmixed blessing, as the swelling number of *Ski-doos* are threatening to make our winter woods as unpleasant as the outboard motor has made our summer lakes.

French-Canadian inventors seem to specialize in odd vehicles. Arthur Sicard did pioneering work on snowblowers, and holds basic patents on this type of machine. And the Thibaults, at Pierreville, south of Montreal, have been building fire engines for Canada for half a century.

Malcolm Dion and his brother developed the *Scoot* in Ontario's Georgian Bay around 1947. This is a sledlike boat driven by an air propeller. It successfully solved the problem of bringing supplies to the islands off the Georgian Bay mainland in the spring and late fall, when the ice was strong enough to prevent the passage of ordinary boats, yet not strong enough to support an automobile. This type of vehicle, now called a "swamp buggy," is used extensively in the Florida Everglades.

Rinaldo Boissonault, who worked for Sicard Inc. for many years improving the snowplow and various types of large snowblowers, holds a patent on the *Sanivan* which is used in many major cities for collecting garbage. Because of these and other key patents, Sicard Inc. has become a major Quebec industry, partly financed by the famous European firm of Schneider & Creusot.

Ski-doos lined up at Sault Ste. Marie for the Ontario international championships, 1967.

Over snow or slush, as well as over water, wonder vehicles like Canadair's Fisher *(right) are making Canada's woods traversable even in the thaw.*

Below, a snow tractor swathing a wide new path into the dense bushlands.

Intensive tests in 1962 proved to the U.S. Army that Canada's scat-cat Jiger *could outclimb and outmatch larger and more expensive vehicles.*

The 'Giraffe' from B.C.

Two western Canadian inventors have made important contributions to off-road vehicles capable of moving over rough country, whether or not there is snow. W. E. Thornton-Trump, of Oliver, British Columbia, has applied his concept of the Dynastat wheel to many radical off-road vehicles. This wheel is powered by a radial motor inside the rim. It provides extremely high torque at low r.p.m., and is beautifully simple, having eliminated the clutch, transmission, differential and other parts which give trouble in rough going. This machine provides a practical power source for wheels up to 15 feet in diameter.

Thornton-Trump now has some 27 specialized wheeled vehicles used in many important industries and manufactured under license in 43 different countries. Among the best known are the *Giraffe* – a wheeled ve-

hicle which provides an aerial platform raised and lowered by hydraulic power – and the *Ridgerunner* – a four-wheel vehicle capable of carrying heavy loads in rough country.

Bruce Nodwell, of Calgary, has developed a prosperous company specializing in tracked carriers. The largest of these machines has four axles, as well as very wide tracks on each side. Originally developed to carry seismic crews searching for oil, these machines were capable of moving drill outfits weighing five tons over the soupy muskeg of Canada's North. With its full load on board, the drill rig carrier operated with less than two pounds per square inch of pressure on the ground. Using the vehicles, oil companies have been able to carry on year-round explorations in the North; formerly, they had to wait until the muskeg froze solid and had to be sure of getting the equipment out again before the spring thaw. If they were caught in the

muskeg, rigs, trucks and equipment would simply disappear.

Nodwell carriers have been used in the Antarctic by scientific expeditions, and in North Carolina where they have helped turn the muskeg-like coastal plains into profitable farm land. In the Lake Phelps area, hundreds of acres of flat, heavily brush-covered swamp land have been drained, cleared and plowed on Nodwell tracks. When the project is completed, over 100,000 waste acres will have been transformed into productive soybean, corn and livestock land.

Canada's inventive contributions to the off-road vehicle capable of running on water, swamp, snow or bush run the gamut from small one-man hunting and trapping vehicles to large troop carriers. While some research was done in the 1940s, it was only in the Fifties that these special vehicles began to achieve military and economic significance.

The Rat *is a miniature train that can travel where there are no tracks, towing its individual cars up hills and around corners that no locomotive could negotiate. Its power comes from a Volkswagen engine.*

The advent of the snow tractor and carrier (below) *is helping Canadians unlock the treasure chest of the Far North, by making year-round explorations possible.*

Snowblowers keep the traffic moving not only on the roads, but in the skies: they have proved vital in clearing the runways of Canada's airports in winter. Above: one in action at Ottawa's Uplands Airport.

Two of the most recent inventions in this field afford an interesting contrast. The Canadair *Rat* carries ten men and sells for $18,000. The *Jiger*, made by the Jiger Corporation, Toronto, carries one man and sells for $1,000. Both vehicles run equally well on land, snow, muskeg, water or swamp.

The *Rat* was designed by a research team under L. Stypinski in 1956. Its purpose was to provide the Canadian Army with a light tracked vehicle capable of carrying a load itself and towing infantry sleds and toboggans over snow-covered northern terrain. The main engineering feature of the *Rat* is its successful use of the principle of steering by articulation. That is, the two halves of the vehicle are brought together at a flexible joint so that the front half can be turned at an angle to the rear half, thus permitting it to turn corners like a snake. This method of steering by articulation, combined with the very low

ground bearing pressure, gives the vehicle an inherent stability uncommon in other types of tracked vehicles. This is particularly noticeable in deep snow, mud and muskeg.

The *Rat* is amphibious with its sealed body, and its tracks provide sufficient propulsion in water to move it at a fair speed. What particularly distinguishes the *Rat* is its fantastically low ground pressure of a half-pound per square inch. This is the lowest ever achieved by any power-driven vehicle, being equivalent to the pressure of a man on a pair of snow shoes. Some idea of just how low this is can be gained when we realize that heavy tracked vehicles now in production vary from 10 to 15 pounds per square inch, while most light-weight vehicles are seldom lower than three pounds.

Canadair is also undertaking development of an off-road vehicle invented by Gordon Fisher, a former Ford Motor Company of Canada en-

gineer. A light fibre-glass machine powered by a tiny 9 h.p. engine, it uses seventeen low-pressure tires to carry it over fantastic obstacles like a tiny sloth. In spite of its odd motion, the Fisher vehicle is capable of reasonable speed – 12 m.p.h. on a hard surface, five or six on snow or mud, and three miles an hour on water.

The pioneer vehicle of this type was invented by John Gower, who in the late 1950s produced his *Jiger*. This fibre-glass six-wheeled vehicle seems to be able to go almost anywhere. It climbs forty-five degree hills on super balloon tires that carry so little pressure they are blown up by mouth. In 1962, in u.s. Army tests near Detroit, the *Jiger* caused a sensation by out-performing many gigantic and expensive American off-road vehicles. Powered by its two 6 h.p. chain-saw-type engines, the Canadian *Jiger* excelled in swamp crossing, hill climbing and plowing through mud.

29

2/ THE AERONAUTS
Conquering the sky

Today, when we jet casually across oceans or commute 400 miles to do a single day's work, we forget that mastery of the air was won the hard way, with sweat and paralyzing fear and crushing disappointment and, on many occasions, sudden death. Canadian inventors have made important contributions to world aviation. At every stage, from the earliest teetering balloon flights to the latest vertical takeoff and landing aircraft, Canadians have shown the imagination and courage needed to break new ground. Turnbull's variable-pitch propeller, Bell's Aerial Experiment Association, Noorduyn's *Norseman* and Avro's *Jetliner* have earned a secure place in world aviation history.

At about the same time that Alexander Graham Bell was beginning his experiments with kites at Baddeck, a young man with just as much dedication but no scientific training was flying kites in what is now Saskatchewan. By 1904, stimulated by newspaper accounts of what the Wright brothers had done, William Gibson turned to making model airplanes. He flew model aircraft successfully but always in the early morning before any of his neighbours arose because, as a respected citizen of a small town, he was afraid of getting a bad name as a crackpot. Late in 1904 he started to build an engine of his own design. Unluckily, he had an attack of the railway fever which was sweeping the country at the time.

As a young merchant with some capital, Gibson decided to take a contract for a twenty-mile stretch of the Grand Trunk Pacific, hoping to make his fortune. But something went wrong, and this time the profit-and-loss system dealt him a loss. In his own words: "When I had the banks cleaned up – or rather, they had cleaned me – I had no stores and no farm. So with what capital I had left I decided to go to the West Coast and start anew."

Gibson was the type of inventor who will not take "no" for an answer. Arriving in Victoria, British Columbia, late in 1906, he heard of a gold mine for sale for $500. He took a look, satisfied himself that the gold was there, worked the mine until he took out gold worth $1,200, then sold the whole property for $10,000. Using this cash, he began in 1908 to build a flying machine.

William Gibson and his first aircraft engine, which he began developing in Balgonie, Sask., and completed in Victoria, B.C. This particular motor was never used on an airplane, but it served as a prototype for a second, successful one.

In spite of the ridicule of his fellow citizens of Victoria, who took no pains to hide the fact they thought him insane, Gibson built the first successful aircraft engine in Canada in March 1910. It developed about 60 h.p. One important feature of the Gibson twin plane – the first aircraft to use the new engine – was that it had contra-rotating propellers. This may have been the first use of contra-rotating propellers in North America.

In September 1910, the twin plane made a successful flight of about 200 feet, with Gibson at the controls. Since Bell's *Silver Dart* had an engine built in New York State, to Gibson goes the honour of having made the first free flight in Canada in a Canadian-built airplane. The distance, 200 feet, sounds little enough to us now but in 1910 it was a major accomplishment. A. V. Roe in England had achieved fame in 1908 with a first flight of only 100 feet. The Wright brothers' first flight was 120 feet under power, and Santos Dumont had flown less than 200 feet in 1906 when making the first heavier-than-air flight in Europe.

Bell's brain trust

At the very height of the age of the private inventor, when Thomas Alva Edison was performing his well-publicized miracles in New Jersey, and men like Wallace Turnbull were working quietly in private laboratories, Nova Scotia saw the earliest beginnings of a powerful new idea. This was the research team – the gathering of highly qualified men, each with different skills, to focus attention on one set of problems. Bell

had become wealthy from his shrewd handling of the basic telephone patents. In addition, he had married into a rich family– the Hubbards of Boston – and was in a position to devote his life to doing exactly what he wanted to do, whether it paid or not. From 1886, he spent his vacations at Baddeck and, in 1892, he built a permanent home there.

Even as a boy, Bell had been interested in what was called "aerial locomotion." The problem was to design a kite light enough to be supported by the air but strong enough to carry a man and a motor. In addition, some form of control for lateral stability had to be devised. One basic problem was the primitive gasoline motors of the day. Developing less than one horsepower for every ten pounds of weight, and being bulky and unpredictable, the engines available seemed hopeless.

In 1901 Bell settled on the tetrahedral cell – three rectangular plane surfaces arranged in a triangular shape. The *Frostking*, which contained 1,300 cells, supported the weight of a man in a ten-mile breeze when demonstrated in 1905. At the height of the tetrahedral cell experiments, a new cottage industry developed in Cape Breton as hundreds of farm homes got into the production of kite cells. These were slender frames of spruce, bamboo or aluminum which the women covered with silk.

At the same time, Bell carried on research on airplane propellers, building scores of different sizes and shapes and testing them on a whirling table. Many of these propellers can be seen today at the Bell Museum at Baddeck.

Up to 1906, Bell had worked in the conventional manner of the individual inventor. He hired workmen and technicians to carry out his orders and make models according to his designs. That summer, however, he made a radical change by gathering together a group of men, each one expert in one aspect of the field of aeronautics. The first was John A. D. McCurdy, an engineering graduate of the University of Toronto, a son of one of Bell's workmen. McCurdy got his friend F. W. "Casey" Baldwin, Toronto graduate in mechanical engineering, and soon thereafter two young Americans were added to the group. In view of the need for engine power, the group brought in Glen H. Curtiss, a young motorcycle manufacturer from Hammondsport, New York. Bell tried to get the Canadian Government to send an official observer to join the group, but it was not interested. The next year, though, the u.s. Government assigned Lieutenant Thomas Selfridge to go to Baddeck and assist.

In October 1907, Mrs. Bell put up money for the Aerial Experiment Association. Mrs. Bell's dollars, Bell's genius and long experience, and the enthusiasm of four young men soon got results. In the last days of that year, the giant man-carrying kite, *Cygnet*, was towed by a steamer along Baddeck Bay carrying Selfridge to the unprecedented height of 168 feet. Now, Bell had a pretty clear idea of how much power was required to lift a large tetrahedral cell kite carrying a man and, while the unit had great strength and lightness, it had the serious drawback of very high wind resistance, or drag. These experiments

On March 12, 1908, Frederick "Casey" Baldwin had good reason to flash this big smile. That day at Hammondsport, N.Y., the 26-year-old became the first Canadian and first British subject to fly an airplane.

guided the team when they built their first powered aircraft – a biplane – in the winter of 1907-08.

The first public flight in North America (all the Wright experiments had been secret) was made in this aircraft, the *Redwing*. Baldwin flew it 318 feet over the ice of Lake Keuka on March 12, 1908, the first British subject and the seventh human being to fly. The *Redwing* was a total loss in a crash five days later, but within two months the group had built a second aeroplane, the *Whitewing*, which had a steerable tricycle under-carriage. This was a genuine world first: tricycle gear with steerable nose wheel is standard today.

It is the flight of the *Silver Dart* that marks the real beginning of Canadian aviation. This, the fifth airplane of the Aerial Experiment Association, was begun at Hammondsport in the summer of 1908 and completed at Baddeck early in 1909. It had a more powerful Curtiss engine and a new type of rubber sealant for the silk-covered wings. On February 23, 1909, with McCurdy at the controls, it took off from the ice of Baddeck Bay and flew nearly half a mile. A few days later, a flight of eight miles was accomplished in about 11 minutes.

Bell's A.E.A. group founded the first aircraft manufacturing company in Canada in March 1909. One of the aircraft they built was tested by the Canadian Army at Petawawa in the summer of 1909. McCurdy, the pilot, found the rough field of Ontario not as simple to land on as the ice in Baddeck Bay, and the aircraft broke up on landing. McCurdy escaped with a broken nose.

Alexander Graham Bell's Oionos, a gliding cellular kite named after the Greek "bird of augury," and his other famous tetrahedral kites were the big hit of the Aero Club of America's exhibition in New York, 1906. He used them to study which type of surface gave the best flying lift, but to the citizens of Baddeck, N.S., where he flew them, they were an eccentric old man's toys – " lot of thing-ma-jigs," a local boatman called them.

The wings that cleave
the northern skies

The great name in bush flying is that of Bob Noorduyn, a Dutchman who studied aeronautics in England and Holland and then came to Canada from the United States. In Montreal, in 1934 he developed definite ideas about an airplane of his own. Talking to operators of mining camps and other bush operations, Noorduyn realized there was a demand for a high-wing single-engine aircraft that could carry heavy loads and get in and out of confined spaces.

The Noorduyn *Norseman*, designed to fill these requirements, became the universal workhorse of the North, just as the Douglas DC3 became the workhorse of the airlines. Like the DC3, the *Norseman* was perfectly suited to its times. Nearly a thousand were built, and most of them are still in use all over the world. Although more powerful engines were put in as they became available, the basic aerodynamic design remained the same from the time the first one was produced in 1934 to the present time. It was the first true bush plane, and a genuine contribution to world aeronautics.

The long Canadian tradition as the supplier of rugged bush aircraft to the rest of the world is today being carried on by DeHavilland of Canada. In the 1950s its single-engined *Beaver* began to compete effectively with the *Norseman*. In the early Sixties, the company announced the new twin-engined *Caribou*. The original *Caribou* used two piston engines but, in 1963, after two years of intensive testing, it was fitted with General Electric turboprop jet engines. De-Havilland has now sold several hundred all over the world.

A Norseman, anchored at Minto Lake, Quebec, 1945.

A big plus in the bush country is the Beaver's *ability to carry heavy loads.*

The latest Turbo Beaver boasts a steep take-off, ideal for small lakes.

After World War I, Canada began to seriously look to her North, and prepare to advance to the last frontier. The age of the voyageur in his canoe was long past, and the new explorers came on wings, searching for oil and minerals, or timber wealth. Pilots combed the bush, the land of lakes and muskeg with rickety airplanes, left-overs of the war. They came in three-seater Avro's, in the flying-boat HS2L's, in Fokkers and the big metal Junkers. It was hazardous flying, often just above the treetops, surveying the ground, or on forest patrols, and delivering supplies – anything from cows to cribs – to isolated settlements. A new breed of flyer was born – the bush pilot – but in time he found he needed a new type of airplane for his work, hardy craft that could handle well in tight spaces, capable of landing on ice or water, or on rough ground. The pioneer of the Canadian-built bush planes was the Norseman, the first one manufactured at Montreal in 1934. In the 1950s DeHavilland came out with a single-engined airplane tailored for Canadian conditions; even its name was as distinctively Canadian as you could get – the Beaver. It was followed by the Caribou, which in 1963 put the bush plane into a new league when it was fitted with turboprop jet engines. Other countries were quick to recognize the worth of Canada's aircraft, and before long their trim shapes were familiar on the skyways of the world.

The Caribou *adapted as a troop carrier...*

As a cargo-carrier in the Far North.

The Avro Jetliner *took to the sky on its maiden flight on August 10, 1949, giving Canada a magnificent headstart in the race to produce a commercial jet airliner. The Jetliner was the first transport jet in North America, second in the world only to Britain's* Comet. *When it made its debut in the U.S. in 1950, it won praise and plaudits from every corner . . . but Ottawa was strangely silent. The Canadian Government was unimpressed. Political paralysis set in: the* Jetliner *was grounded and scrapped, and Canada was out of the race altogether.*

The New York

Copyright, 1950, by The New York Times Company.

Entered as Second-Class Matter.
Post Office, New York, N. Y.

NEW YORK, WEDNESDAY, APRIL 19, 1950

L DELIVERY HOMES SET AL ECONOMY

tes Budget Slash, Service Is Also Parcel Post

K-UPS REDUCED

Areas Lose Trip rs—10,000 Jobs Union Protests

LAWRENCE
n New York Times.
ON, April 18—In a
my move, Postmas-
se M. Donaldson to-
sidential mail deliv-
to one a day and
s in postal service.
on said the action
o curtail a mount-
he operation of the
partment. He also
'ter cuts in the Post
were made by a
e.
as assailed at once
tion of Letter Car-
as "a rape of the
" The association
rotest to Congress.
son's order was
thirty-six-point di-
ay's issue of The
, which most post-
receive tomorrow
effective immedi-

Probably Lost
e Post Office De-
ied to estimate how
ild be lost as a re-
nomy order, but an
e said tonight that
d 10,000 as a "good
uctions will be made

First Jet Liner Seen Here
Flies From Toronto in Hour

The Avro jet liner in flight over Idlewild airport
The New York Times (by Sam Falk)

The Avro jet liner, the first tur-
bojet transport plane ever flown in
the United States, arrived yester-
day at New York International
Airport, Idlewild, Queens, after a
flight from Toronto that took
slightly less than one hour.

The sleek new air liner received
a prolonged welcome from the several hundred spectators who gathered at the airport to witness its
first landing outside of Canada,
where it was built by a company
formed only four years ago.

Carrying three crew members,
three passengers and the world's
first "jet-borne" airmail, the four-
engined plane set a record for the
365-mile flight from Moulton Airport, Toronto, to Idlewild.

Piloted by Donald H. Rogers,
chief test pilot for A. V. Roe Canada, Ltd., manufacturer of the
sixty-passenger airliner, the jet
liner's departure from Toronto was
clocked at 9:30:04 A. M. It arrived at Idlewild at exactly 10:30
A. M., making its flight time fifty-
nine minutes and fifty-six seconds.

Mr. Rogers said he spent the
first twelve minutes in the air
climbing to a cruising altitude of
20,000 feet. From that point on
his average speed was 400 miles
an hour. For a short time he was
making 425 miles an hour, aided by
a tail wind.

One of the passengers, Gordon
R. McGregor, president of Trans-

Continued on Page 23, Column 2

CRIPPS DASHES HOPE OF TAXATION RELIEF IN BRITISH BUDGET

Only Lowest Income Bracket
Gets Slight Concession —
No Industrial Palliative

WELFARE COSTS LIMITED

Food Subsidies Are Reduced
—Gasoline Doubled, Price Up
—Better Beer Promised

By RAYMOND DANIELL
Special to The New York Times

LONDON, April 18—Once more
Sir Stafford Cripps, Chancellor of
the Exchequer, hammered home
the lesson today that the welfare
state meant sacrifice as well as
benefits. He announced that its
whole cost must be met out of
revenue, or, in other words, that
the taxpayers must foot the oill.

This dashed all hope of substantial tax relief although Sir Stafford, presenting his new budget to
the House of Commons, did man-
age to lower the burden slightly on
income taxpayers in the lowest income brackets.

His budget, calling for revenue
of £3,897,800,000, however contained no palliatives for industry,
the middle class or the harassed
housewife.

[The £3,897,800,000 figure is
equivalent to $10,913,840,000 at
the current exchange rate of
$2.80 to £1, but in terms of the
British internal economy £1 (20
shillings or 240 pence) repre-
sents more than $2.80 in pur-
chasing power.]

Some Save Shilling a Year

The relief that Sir Stafford
granted to the long-suffering British income taxpayers fell upon all
in accordance with the Labor par-

M'CARTHY SUBMITS 2 MORE WITNESSES

Former F.B.I. Undercover Man
and Ex-Agent Are Named
to Testify on Lattimore

'NEW THINKING' SEEN ON ATOM CONTROLS

McMahon Says Congressional
Restudy of U. S. Plan Spurs
Administration to Ponder

First and last Jetliner

The first commercial jet in North America, and the second (by only two weeks) in the world, was the Avro *Jetliner*, designed and built at Toronto. In early 1950 it caused a sensation by flying from Toronto to New York in half the time taken by the conventional planes of the day. This was the first appearance of a jet transport anywhere in the United States, and the first time in the world that air mail had been carried by jet. The New York newspapers carried excited reports.

Later, when the *Jetliner* flew from Chicago to New York in one hour and forty-two minutes, at a speed of 459 miles an hour, a u.s. syndicated columnist wrote:

"This should give our nation a good healthful kick in its placidity. The fact that our massive but under-populated good neighbour to the north has a mechanical product that licks anything of ours is just what the doctor ordered for our over-developed ego. The Canadian plane's feat accelerates a process already begun in this nation – a realization that Uncle Sam has no monopoly on genius, that our products are not necessarily the best simply because we made them."

At a time when u.s. pure jets were still at the drawing-board stage, Canada had one hopping about between u.s. cities and going through its spectacular paces before the u.s.a.a.f.

Test pilots' reports on the handling characteristics of the *Jetliner*, the C102, were uniformly enthusiastic. The authoritative u.s. publication, *American Aviation*, wrote:

The Jetliner's *first Toronto-New York flight cut the flying time to 60 minutes – half the time of ordinary planes.*

". . . The plane operated for two years without a single sign of any problem that would have stunted its future. Its speed would have eliminated any serious airline thought of ever buying DC7s and, in the light of the later (British) *Comet* grounding, the c102 would have had the jet transport market pretty much to itself for three or four years and sold in the hundreds on world markets."

Many aviation experts think, had it been properly handled, the *Jetliner* would have been the DC3 of the jet age. It was a simple aircraft, requiring very little maintenance. Moreover, it was cheap.

Why was this gold mine, that could have been a source of endless pride to every Canadian, abandoned at the height of its fame? When asked this question in parliament, Cabinet Minister C. D. Howe offered a lame explanation to the effect that it was not a good engineering concept, and that the plane required sand as a weight in its tail before it would fly. Every prototype aircraft uses sandbags to distribute the centre of gravity for test purposes. Not well designed? The Americans awarded James Floyd the Wright medal for his *Jetliner* design. This is the Nobel Prize of the aviation world, and Floyd was the first non-American ever to win it.

Top executives of Air Canada argue that the change of power plants made the *Jetliner* useless for their operations. The original design called for two Rolls-Royce Avon jet engines, but these were not ready in time for the prototype, so the design was changed to use four Rolls-Royce Derwent centrifugal jets. These required more fuel and produced less power, hence could not satisfy Air Canada's reserve requirements, especially for the critical Toronto-Winnipeg run.

Air Canada at that time was highly cautious, demanding, for example, on the New York-Toronto flight that the jet carry sufficient fuel to fly to New York, stay stacked for one hour above the airport, fly back to Toronto and still have a full reserve of fuel left. That is, out of 30,000 pounds of fuel, less than 10,000 was to be used for the flight, with 20,000 for the safety factor. Many people in the industry feel that this requirement was too conservative and, in fact, even on trans-Atlantic flights such standards are not in force today.

Technical arguments against the *Jetliner* don't seem to hold water, as far as I am concerned, and the political explanation is hardly more convincing. When the Korean War broke out there was a need for the CF100 jet fighter, also manufactured by Avro. C. D. Howe apparently felt that Avro could not build a production jet fighter and at the same time do further development work on the *Jetliner*. National Airlines of the U.S. was prepared to place a firm order for four of the machines, but C. D. Howe insisted that Avro could not accept the order until it had built a number of the CF100s. This seems to have been an irrational decision, because plenty of aircraft companies handle military and civilian production lines side by side.

About the same time, Howe ordered two *Comet* jet transports from the United Kingdom for the R.C.A.F. The reason given was that they were to serve as interception practice ships for the CF100s but they were never used as targets, and when they arrived from England they were fitted up as executive transport for VIPs. If two *Jetliners* had been bought for this purpose for which, being as fast as the *Comet*, they would have served admirably, that sale alone would have set the *Jetliner* up in business. With a firm order from National Airlines, and an increasing interest and enthusiasm from the U.S.A.A.F., a Canadian jet aircraft industry would have been well under way.

In 1951, work on the partially completed second *Jetliner* was halted. Some time later the original CF-EJO-X, which had flown to the major airports of the United States to such applause, was scrapped. No Canadian official or private museum was interested, but there was a plan to obtain it for the Smithsonian Institution in Washington. Finally this idea too, fell through.

James Floyd came to Canada from England in 1946 to work on the Jetliner *design from the outset. Previously, he had worked on the* Lancaster, Anson *and* Hawker Hotspur.

October 4, 1957 – sleek and shiny, the first Arrow rolled onto a runway at Malton, Ont. That same day, Russia launched her first Sputnik.

The 'Arrow' that fell

Seven years later, at the greatest moment in the whole history of Canadian technology, we did it again. This time, the victim was the Canadian jet fighter plane, the powerful *Arrow*. On March 25, 1958, with Avro's chief development pilot Jan Zurakowski at the controls, the CF105 *Arrow* flew for the first time. The aircraft was magnificent, taking off and landing without a hitch.

After all the heartbreaking difficulties and obstacles that had been overcome, Avro's 14,000 men and women took it – as well they might – as a personal triumph. Morale was high and it looked as if, for the first time, Canada was going to make a lasting mark on world technology and get credit for it.

Then, at 4 p.m. on September 24, 1958, Prime Minister John Diefenbaker suddenly announced that the *Arrow* programme was cancelled. Avro president Crawford Gordon announced over the public-address system that afternoon that Avro's 14,000 people were now unemployed. Canada lost a priceless pool of talent as nearly all the technical staff quickly got jobs in the U.S.

Six of the jobless engineers stayed in Canada, however, and formed Avian Aircraft Limited, of Georgetown, Ontario. After overcoming initial technical and financial disasters, they got their "gyroplane" into the air in 1962. This is a vertical takeoff and landing (VTOL) aircraft that can make a sudden 30-foot jump from the ground and then fly away. This enables it to land in, or take off from, a parking lot.

March 25, 1958 – a time of triumph for test pilot Jan Zurakowski, after the Arrow's *first flight. It could soar at 1,000 miles per hour.*

TORONTO DAILY STAR

METRO
Saturday: Mi
tonight 10, high

FRIDAY, FEBRUARY 20, 1959—54 PAGES

10¢ PER COPY. 55

Diefenbaker Decides:

'SCRAP ARROW'

'No Other Work For Makers of Arrow Or Engines'--Ottawa

By BRUCE MACDONALD
Star Staff Correspondent

Ottawa, Feb. 20—The federal government has scrapped the Avro Arrow and its Iroquois engine, Prime Minister Diefenbaker announced in the House of Commons today.

At the same time the prime minister made it clear that the government has no alternative air defence system planned to take the place of the supersonic jet interceptor, raising the threat that thousands of employees of the A. V. Roe and Orenda Engine companies will be thrown out of work.

Commons Hushed

Mr. Diefenbaker, making the announcement to a hushed House of Commons at the opening today, indicated the government's decision to abandon the Arrow was due to a rapidly diminishing need for interceptors and the estimated $7,800,000 cost for 100 aircraft.

Prime Minister Diefenbaker also disclosed that the government is also negotiating with the U.S. for the right to acquire nuclear warheads with which to arm the Bomarc ground-to-air guided missiles.

For Full Potential

"The full potential of these defensive weapons is achieved only when they are armed with nuclear warheads," the prime minister asserted.

"The government is, therefore, examining with the U.S. government questions connected with the acquisition of nuclear warheads for Bomarc and other defensive weapons used by the Canadian forces in Canada and the storage of warheads in Canada." The same question was also being taken up with regard to providing nuclear-armed weapons for Canadian forces in Europe.

It is likely that in addition to the Bomarc, the government is also seeking nuclear warheads for the Lacrosse, a ground-to-ground guided missile being acquired from the U.S. for the army, and the Sidewinder air-to-air guided missile, already in service with the naval air arm.

Against U.S. Law

At present U.S. law prohibits the U.S. government from making the warheads available to Canada. The only way they now could be supplied was if they were under the control of

ARROW'S END MAY SERIOUSLY HURT BUILDERS

Special to The Star

Malton, Feb. 20—Contractors and sub-contractors here see the cancellation of the Arrow program as meaning the end of Orenda Engines Ltd., a sister company of Avro Aircraft.

The Orenda company, which has been tooled to produce engines for the Arrow, is, with Avro Aircraft, a subsidiary of A. V. Roe (Canada) Ltd.

At the Avro plant a blackout was imposed on news and a hurriedly called meeting of senior executives went into session.

The public address system gave out one brief announcement. Employees in the sprawling plant were told no official word had been received but it appeared the government was dropping the Arrow. It was stated a second announcement would be made this afternoon.

This was taken by many employees to indicate Avro might announce plans for a new project.

A pretty Avro receptionist was close to tears when she learned of the cancellation. Most employees, however, accepted the announcement without showing emotion. There were no shouts of protest.

When the government first said last September it would

Down The Drain

'Unjustified,' is Reply To Finnish Charges

AFRICANS RIOT FREE PRISONER FLY IN TROOPS

Salisbury, Southern Rhodesia, Feb. 20 — AP — Troops and police reinforcements were flown today to Karonga, Nyasaland, where Africans rioted and freed a prisoner from the jail.

Sir Roy Welensky, prime

ight is his mother. Rifle lies which came out during struggle the provincial officer's foot
Star Photo by Federal Newsphotos

GIVE ROBERTS GAMBLING DEN NAMES--MACKEY

Metro Police Chief James Mackey said today he is prepared to give Attorney-General Kelso Roberts the names of social clubs which are controlled in their directorates by professional gamblers.

The attorney-general asked the Metro chief to meet him and discuss comments the chief made in a panel discussion Wednesday night. Chief Mackey suggested gamblers operated full-scale under the guise of private clubs.

Mr. Roberts told The Star he would take action to suspend a club's license if the chief had sufficient evidence.

May Mention Tapping

Chief Mackey suggested he may also bring up the subject of wire-tapping. He said he would reiterate his private views that the police might in certain cases run down gamblers by getting a fiat or some other legal instrument which would allow them to tap telephone wires.

Before the conference began Mr. Roberts said he believed Chief Mackey was merely pointing out the difficulties of enforcing anti-gambling laws when he mentioned Wednesday night at a panel discussion that bona fide clubs become dens for gamblers after under-the-table charter exchanges.

As the two men met, CCF leader Donald C. MacDonald said that if the attorney-general was going to look into this question, he should also inquire into "the activities of professional operators who have gained control of bingo clubs" in the province.

"I can see no reason, either morally or legally, why any organization engaged in public service of whatever kind should be denied the right to raise funds through bingo parties — particularly when there are so many people who enjoy playing the game," he said.

"But this situation has gotten out of hand. In some instances it has grown to be big business with the operation of the parties now in the hands of professionals.

February 20, 1959 — the final axe had fallen. The Arrow would be scrapped because of "a rapidly diminishing need for interceptors."

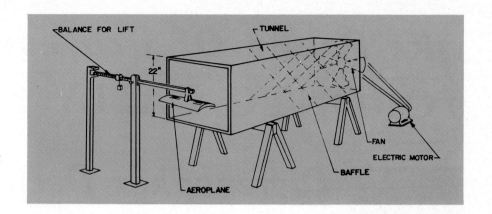

Using this wind tunnel, Wallace Rupert Turnbull made the discovery that upward slanted wings gave airplanes better stability than the straight-built types of the time.

The variable-pitch propeller. A motor mounted on the hub controlled the blades.

Genius in the woodshed

Canada's most important contribution to world aviation was made by a man whom few schoolboys today could even name. Some experts believe his work to be perhaps the most important single invention in the history of aeronautics. Working alone in a woodshed behind his old-fashioned house in Rothesay, New Brunswick, Wallace Rupert Turnbull came up with the variable-pitch propeller. It made the air transport industry possible.

Before 1920, airplanes could fly but could not carry a payload because they lacked the equivalent of the automobile gearshift. If engine speed and propeller pitch (that is, the angle of the blades) were right for take-off, power was then wasted in straight and level flight. On the other hand, if pitch and r.p.m. were right for straight and level flight, the plane could not get off the ground. Turnbull made and demonstrated the first practical controllable-pitch propeller with the system of manual or automatic pitch control still in use today.

Born in 1870 at Saint John, Turnbull graduated in engineering from Cornell, studied at Heidelberg, and returned to Canada to set up his private research laboratory at Rothesay. Here, in 1902, our first pioneer in scientific aviation built one of the earliest wind tunnels in America, a railroad to test propellers, and, as his crowning achievement, the variable-pitch propeller. Turnbull was Canada's most successful native-born private inventor. He worked on inventions all his life, always made a good living, and died comparatively wealthy. When he died in 1954 he had been working on the problems of harnessing the Bay of Fundy tides.

During World War I, Turnbull went to England and it was there that he began to think about the basic problem of the variable-pitch propeller. To operate efficiently under varying conditions of flight, the propeller itself had to be changed in some way. Obviously, the only ways a propeller could be changed during flight would be to adjust the pitch or the length of the blades.

By 1916 the Canadian had a working model put together which controlled the pitch of the propeller by foot brakes in the cockpit. Early in 1918 he succeeded, after several demonstrations to the British Government, in getting a contract to develop his propeller, but he had hardly started when the war ended and the contract was cancelled.

Another man might have been disheartened, but Turnbull carried his first R.A.F. propeller home from England and, by 1920, had it working well.

After the usual delays in getting the armed services and government agencies interested, the propeller was finally brought to trial at Camp Borden in 1923. After only the ground trials had been completed, a hangar at Camp Borden was destroyed by fire and the only variable-pitch propeller in the world went up in flames.

Again, Turnbull set doggedly to work, and within two years had a new model with an electric motor to make the blade pitch adjustment. In 1927 the Royal Canadian Air Force successfully flight-tested this unit, the world's first variable-pitch propeller.

Installed on an Avro biplane, Turnbull's variable-pitch propeller was flight tested for the first time on June 6, 1927. Above: Turnbull (right) *with his invention.*

Turnbull used a trolley on a home-made railway track (left) *to test models of fixed-pitch propellers.*

3 / THE SEEKERS
The size and the shape

Inventions never come out of the wilderness or the jungle. The known technology must first be applied to the new territory to make roads, canals, industries – all the basic services men need before they can make a living. After the Treaty of Paris was signed in 1763, the victorious British appointed Samuel Holland surveyor-general of the colony. He and his men made accurate surveys so farm land could be allocated to demobilized soldiers and other would-be colonists; he calculated the fall of rivers and set up the best routes for what was to remain for another hundred years the basic transportation system; and, most important, he made the topographical surveys used to locate roads for settlement and trade. Thus, for the years between 1760 and 1860, established skills – mostly from England – were applied to make Canada habitable. Once this was done, genuine inventions began to appear.

The first major improvement was a badly needed rebuilding of the roads. In the 1760s the new merchants of Quebec appealed to the government to stop the inhabitants from parking their waggons in such a way as to block the roads – the earliest Canadian example of the parking problem. A decade later the roads to Albany and Boston from Montreal had been rebuilt so thoroughly that they could be used even by carriages.

Changes now came quickly. Benjamin Franklin came to Quebec City and opened post offices there, in Three Rivers and in Montreal. Soon afterwards, a monthly courier service was set up between Montreal and New York. This allowed mail to get on board British ships bound for London, even during the winter when the St. Lawrence was closed. The mail travelled between Montreal and Quebec once a week; the journey required only thirty hours.

In Upper Canada, roads came later. But, by the beginning of the 19th century, there was a network of main arteries, although contemporary travellers complained about the state of them. They were passable on horseback and could even be traversed by a waggon, given a sufficiently intrepid driver.

Yonge Street was opened from the muddy village of York, now Toronto, to Holland's Landing on Lake Simcoe in 1796. About the same time, Dundas Street had been built from York westerly to London and, in 1800, Asa Danforth had constructed a road to the east as far as the Trent River, near Peterborough. By 1808 the stage coach provided regular service between Montreal and Kingston, and

The Lachine Canal at Montreal, seen here in the 1870s, was a vital link in the St. Lawrence canal chain, though at completion in 1824 the 8½-mile waterlane was only five feet deep.

another service ran between Hamilton and York.

Bypassing the rapids

North America's first canal with locks grew out of this push to improve communications. As early as 1700 there was a contract between Dollier de Casson and Sieur de Catalogne for construction of a canal bypassing the Lachine rapids, but nothing really came of that for over a century. In 1779, however, Captain William Twiss of the British Army, realizing that a canal around the Cedar, Cascades and Coteau Rapids in the St. Lawrence would have important military uses, began construction of a canal at Coteau du Lac. This was finished in 1781.

A considerable acceleration in canal building was made possible by the union of the legislatures of Upper Canada and Lower Canada, 1841.

The invention of the steamship pushed development of canals. Sailing boats were difficult to handle on narrow waterways, but even the earliest steamboats could go anywhere. The rapid increase in sidewheelers and sternwheelers forced an equally swift improvement in the canal system. As transportation improved and goods could be moved more cheaply from one area of Canada to another, trade improved, food prices dropped, and people had more money to spend on comforts.

To cut the Chignecto

For sheer imagination, it is hard to match the Chignecto railway and canal scheme which was actually put

A growing economy, and the appearance of the steam paddlewheeler, made it necessary to enlarge and deepen existing canals. This shows excavation work at Montreal, 1874.

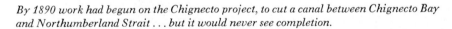

By 1890 work had begun on the Chignecto project, to cut a canal between Chignecto Bay and Northumberland Strait . . . but it would never see completion.

Sir William Logan: geological surveys

Sir Edward Sabine: magnetic fields

Sir Sandford Fleming: farm divisions

in hand in 1889. As far back as 1822, business men and politicians in Nova Scotia were discussing cutting a canal through the narrow neck of land that still separates the Gulf of St. Lawrence from the Bay of Fundy. In 1831 the Chamber of Commerce of Saint John petitioned Governor Sir John Harvey to begin the work.

It was clear to anyone who looked at a map that the distance between trading centres like Quebec City and Saint John would be reduced by over 1,000 miles by cutting a canal a mere 27 miles long – but such a multi-million-dollar scheme was far beyond the power of the Maritimes in the 1830s. Forty years later, however, the Maritimes had achieved wealth through shipbuilding and trade. The Chignecto project came up again and, all through the Seventies, various plans were put forward.

Finally, in the late Eighties, an ingenious combined project was proposed by which part of the distance would be through canals and the remainder (over the height of land) by a unique railway. This railway idea was quite different from anything ever proposed before, or since. The plan was to have tracks strong enough and cars large enough to haul the entire ocean-going ship, complete with its cargo, from the end of one canal to the beginning of the other. Work was actually begun, but when the promoters ran out of money the scheme folded.

Even today, when competing services are vastly improved, the Chignecto canal still seems to make sense. Many people are convinced it would dramatically improve economic conditions in the Maritimes.

The first National Atlas

Since the days of Surveyor-General Holland, map-making and surveying have been raised to fine arts in Canada and we are now recognized abroad as leaders in scientific cartography. It's not surprising that Canadians should be good map-makers as we have an immense and greatly varied territory as raw material. Studies begun in the 18th century, ranging from oceanography to measuring the heights of mountains, culminated in Canada producing the world's first national atlas in 1906.

Undersea mapping – charting the depth of water and the nature of coastlines – had been done after a fashion by the early explorers, but the first systematic study seems to have been made by Joseph Frederick Desbarres in Canadian waters toward

Department of the Interior Canada

HONOURABLE FRANK OLIVER, MINISTER

1906

ATLAS OF CANADA

A world first, the Atlas of Canada *was enlarged in 1915. It included 80 plates of maps and 44 pages of statistical diagrams.*

the end of the 18th century. He was sent by the British Government to do a hydrographic survey of the east coast of North America; he remained to become founder of Sydney, Nova Scotia, and the first lieutenant-governor of Cape Breton.

The first magnetic survey in the world was accomplished by Sir Edward Sabine, of Toronto, in 1839. He set up sensitive apparatus for detecting the changing magnetic field of the earth in Madras, India, Melbourne, Australia, on St. Helena Island and in Toronto. From the continuous recordings of the readings at these four stations, he was able to provide important information on the nature and changing characteristics of the earth's magnetic field.

Another knight – from Montreal this time – was the founder and first director of the geological surveys on which Canada's great mining industry depends. He was Sir William Logan. Educated at Edinburgh University, then the world's centre for geology, Logan revolutionized current concepts of the science more than a century ago. This work is still going on, using equipment such as the helicopter, the airborne magnetometer, and the scintillometer, that Logan, with all his imagination, would probably not have believed. Today, the Geological Survey of Canada sends more than a hundred parties a year into the field to make new maps and bring old ones up to date.

Yet another Canadian knight, Sir Sandford Fleming (an immigrant, he was born in Kirkcaldy, Scotland), offered a surveying innovation aimed at reducing the loneliness that brought early settlers on the Prairies

J. M. Bridgman: aerial photographs

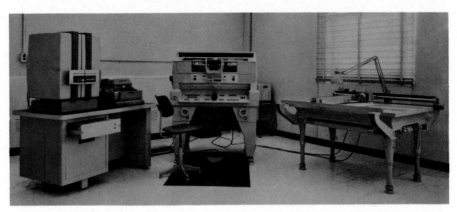

Helava's analytic plotter: it could process photographs taken from space satellites.

to despair. The Canadian survey system was based on the six-mile-square township, which had been adopted from the United States in 1871. Under this system, each square mile of the land was numbered and called a section.

The law passed to encourage the Canadian Pacific Railway to build a transcontinental line granted the railroad all the odd-numbered sections within 24 miles on either side of the main line. The even-numbered sections were reserved for settlers. Each section, containing 640 acres, was subdivided into quarter sections of 160 acres each and this quarter section became the normal allotment of the settler. Sir Sandford's idea was to break the land up into triangular, rather than square, plots of land so that the homesteads of four contiguous properties could be placed together, companionably, at the centre of the section. Although Fleming was Chief Engineer for the Dominion Government, he was unable to get anyone to consider his plan seriously. He wrote wryly to Rudyard Kipling: "They say it is impractical because it has never been done before, a conclusive reason with governments."

One of the little-known sidelights of Canadian history is that the Dominion Observatory, born officially in 1905, really had its beginning in a surveying problem. When the c.p.r. grants were passed, it was realized they could be made only on the basis of careful mapping. This, in turn, could be done only on a sound astronomical basis – the establishment of base lines of longitude and latitude across the country. For this job an astronomer was required.

A surveyor, Dr. Otto Klotz, became the first man to carry the world longitude network westward, linking up with the network established east from Greenwich a generation earlier. Dr. W. F. King worked with Klotz on the practical problem of setting base lines for the railroad survey, and in 1890, was appointed Chief Astronomer for Canada. Out of King's work came the founding of the Dominion Observatory in 1905.

Advances in map-making

Canadian Government laboratories have been particularly active in advancing the art and techniques of map-making. Most of our mapping inventions have been concerned with making the information obtained from the latest methods more easily and quickly translatable into maps.

From aerial photographs, scientists in the Department of Forestry worked out methods of estimating the size of woodlots, and even the type and size of trees. The Department of Mines has had men working on the latest techniques of geological surveying, using airborne instruments.

The Gamble plotter of the 1950s was one of the earliest advances. S. C. Gamble, director of the Surveys and Mapping Branch in Ottawa, invented a serial plotter for a standard photogrammetrical table which greatly speeded-up the process of map-making. It came quickly into commercial production and now enjoys wide use.

J. M. ("Monty") Bridgman joined the Photographic Survey Corporation in Toronto after World War II as head of its technical division. Under

his direction, the company developed airborne magnetometers, cameras, radioactive detection devices, and radar systems for aerial survey. In 1951 he founded p.s.c. Applied Research Ltd., which was taken over by A. V. Roe in 1957. Another group, Canadian Airborne Geophysics Ltd., founded in Toronto by Douglas N. Kendall, does survey work all over the world. One of Kendall's employees, Gilbert L. Hobrough, invented a device called the *Stereomat*. Now being manufactured in the United States, it uses electronic methods of carrying out work normally done by the eye. It makes ten times faster the process of making contour and relief maps from aerial photographs.

The best-known name in Canadian cartography today is U. V. Helava, of the National Research Council. His invention was said by one famous photogrammetrist to "move the science from the bicycle age to the jet age." Helava's device, called an analytic plotter, caused a sensation when it was introduced in Ottawa in 1963. It is the only photogrammetric device that can work with photographs taken from orbiting satellites.

Some years ago it was thought to be a major triumph when experts were able to recognize distinct objects in aerial photographs taken from 30,000 feet. Obviously the higher the camera, the greater the area covered in each sweep. But now that photographs can be taken hundreds of miles up by orbiting satellites, a whole new era of map-making has begun. The Helava machine is basically a computer and uses mathematical principles to convert the photo images into lines on paper.

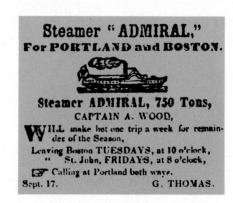
4 / NEW POWER
Making things move

Power is the key to any industrial revolution. In the 19th century Britain led the world because she was first in getting cheap power out of steam; in the 20th century the Russians were first into outer space because they had more powerful propellents. Canada has made vital contributions to the development of two energy sources: hydro-electric power and atomic energy. In addition, Canadians have aided the development of steam and internal-combustion engines.

On the night of November 19, 1853, as a young inventor lay dying of tuberculosis in his father's home on the St. John River, the sky was suddenly ablaze with flame, and the ship *Benjamin Franklin,* powered by his creation, a double-expansion marine steam engine, drifted by. She was ablaze to the water's edge, and had been abandoned by her crew. "Thus", as some unsung poet writing for the Sackville *Tribune* reported, "in the same hour the man and his work, once things of life and beauty, were rendered to dust and ashes." This is the most romantic death scene in the annals of Canadian invention.

The inventor was Benjamin Franklin Tibbetts. His death at 35 cost Canada an imaginative mind of great promise. The monument over his grave at Scotchtown says that he "revolutionized marine engineering." This may be forgiven as an excess of local pride, but it is true in the limited sense that he certainly did revolutionize marine engineering in the Maritimes.

In a small factory in Montreal owned by his uncle, Tibbetts picked up the basic techniques of 19th century steam. His idea was perfectly sound. He wanted to get maximum use out of the steam and therefore used it once in one cylinder under high pressure, and a second time as low-pressure steam in a different cylinder.

By 1842 Tibbetts had found a financial backer, Thomas Pickard, of Fredericton, and he installed a prototype engine in the ship *Reindeer*. This was a fast paddle-wheel steamer with trim lines which, in later years, made many speed records on the St.

The steamer, Admiral; *an 1843 drawing*

Tibbetts: compound marine engine

John River between Fredericton and Saint John. In the New Brunswick *Reporter* for December 12, 1845, there is an advertisement by Tibbetts inviting engineers to see his engine in operation. The next year the New Brunswick Legislature voted to give him one hundred pounds sterling to help him secure a patent.

When Tibbetts made the trek to Washington to try to get a U.S. patent, he found that his device, in essence, was already patented. Local tradition insists that his plans had been stolen, but research at the British Patent Office and the U.S. Patent Office shows that in the two preceding decades the basic idea of the compound marine engine had been well worked over.

A study of Tibbetts' patent drawings and contemporary descriptions of his machine indicate that, while the basic idea was old, his method of embodying it into a machine was both new and ingenious. Like many inventors, Tibbetts suffered from an incurable urge to tinker. The engine became ever more complicated as the inventor got more and more ideas.

His first engine was in use in various ships for seventy years. The *Reindeer* (108 tons) demonstrated both high speed and great economy of fuel. The engine was later transferred to the *Admiral* and then to the *Antelope* and other ships, giving good service until 1914. As late as 1930, the old engine stood in a shed near Saint John, a priceless artifact and illustration of early Canadian technology. Before I could get to it, it was broken up for scrap.

Tibbetts' compound engine did have the disadvantage of too many working parts. The old-fashioned engine taken out of the *Admiral* to be replaced by the Tibbetts model had only five levers and valves; the new engine had 14. This engine, with its long stroke and its myriad of moving rods and wires, must have been something to see.

The force of falling water

The art of making electric power out of running water changed the face of Canada. It was first used to drive the wheels of a Canadian factory in 1888, at Georgetown, Ontario, where John R. Barber installed electric motors to supply extra power for a paper mill. After 1895, the cheap power from Niagara Falls quickly attracted industry and created many thousands of jobs. North American capitalists looking for investment opportunities were not slow to catch on, and hydro-electric plants were established in river valleys all along the east coast of the United States and Canada.

The two great pioneers of hydro-electric power generation and distribution in North America were Canadians. Sir Adam Beck, the engineer from London, Ontario, who fought the private power companies to a standstill and conceived the Ontario Hydro Electric System, was the father of hydro power in North America. His right-hand man, Dr. Thomas H. Hogg, fought the technical battles while Beck laboured on the political front. Between them, they set up in the first sixty years of the present century a unique organization that has served as a model for public power in many parts of the

The pioneer of public power, Adam Beck got his start making cigar boxes in London, Ontario.

Thomas H. Hogg: *"Demand for electricity was found to increase . . . as its price was reduced."*

47

When power became
a public servant

To Adam Beck's thinking, the white water cascading over Niagara Falls was too great a natural resource to be the monopoly of private hydro interests. He hoped to see the Goliath of Niagara working for the people, owned by the people: a radical idea, indeed, coming not from a socialist, but a Conservative M.P.P. In 1905, James Whitney's Conservative Government was swept into office in Ontario with the slogan, "The water power of Niagara should be as free as air."

world. At the same time, they introduced literally hundreds of important technological innovations.

Beck, with his basic concept of cheap power in every home, whether in the city or in the country, and of electric motors driving labour-saving devices, epitomized the hopes that are always raised by any new technology. Electricity, like automation fifty years later, was hailed as the new panacea. It was going to take the drudgery out of housework and the routine work out of offices, and introduce a new era of cleanliness, efficiency and leisure.

Several other Canadian inventors applied their skills to making the "miracle" of electricity a reality. The first demonstration of the use of the new power for cooking in Canada took place in Ottawa in 1891. Thomas Ahearne and Warren Soper, embryo electrical manufacturers, demonstrated their new electric stove at the Windsor Hotel, preparing a gourmet dinner for invited notables.

Rural electrification became technically possible in 1897 when Lacroix opened the first long-distance power transmission in the British Empire. Five years later, Shawinigan Water & Power had built a power transmission line the unheard-of distance of ninety miles, all the way from Shawinigan Falls to Montreal.

A curtain of bubbles

Harnessing water power still brings out fresh inventiveness in Canadians. In 1963, the Ontario Hydro was faced with the problem of removing a plug of rock near the new Sir Adam Beck No. 2 Generating Station at Niagara

In 1912 Adam Beck launched a travelling "circus," sending caravans across rural southwestern Ontario to demonstrate the blessings of electricity. At country fairs and on little farms, electricity – the harnessed giant – was praised, but in that day, it still took horses to pull some of the mobile units.

Kitchener, when it was still called Berlin, became the first Ontario community to switch-on with public hydro. It was a gala day on October 11, 1910, with flags decked on the buildings, and fluttering on the brand-new streetlight standards. In honour of the occasion, City Fathers even had a part of the main street paved.

THE BERLIN NEWS RECORD

WHITNEY AND BECK PRESS BUTTON

Sir James Whitney Declines To Deprive Hon. Adam Beck of the Privilege of Formally Turning On Niagara Power, and Both Perform the Important Function, the Premier Grasping Mr. Beck's Hand and Pressing His Finger on the Button, an Act of Courtesy Which Brought an Outburst of Cheering Almost as Voluminous as the Roar of Niagara Falls—Formal Turning on of Niagara Power in Ontario Was Successfully Carried Out in the presence of About 8000 People, Including Distinguished Visitors from the United States and Canada

The local newspaper proclaimed it "the greatest day in the history of Berlin."

A three-ton Gram truck accompanied two horse-drawn wagons on Beck's "circus" route. It carried something for everyone: for the women, the marvellous new washing machines they had heard so much about; for the men, a chance to put circular saws to the test.

A small turbine plant built here in 1888 by John R. Barber made this paper mill at Georgetown, Ontario, the first plant in the world to be run by hydro-electric power. It was a big step forward . . . although the turbine only generated 100 HP.

Falls. The engineers' dilemma was that a blast large enough to remove the plug at one shot might damage the nearby power house; if they shut the power house down for the blast, they would have to import a million dollars' worth of electricity from the United States during the shutdown period.

Adolphe J. Laprairie, of Toronto, at that time a representative of Canadian Industries Limited's explosives division, came up with the idea of an underwater air barrier. A curtain of bubbles, coming from pipes laid at the bottom of the channel, was arranged between the blast and the generating station. When the blast went off, not even windows rattled in the generating station.

Since then, the patents owned by c.i.l. have been applied to solve many problems of submarine blasting. The shock waves which before used to kill fish, destroy piers, and even injure swimmers, can now be contained safely behind the air curtain. The technique is now used in Europe, in Hawaii, in the Panama Canal, and wherever major underwater blasting is required.

A streetcar that worked

John J. Wright, aided by another Canadian inventor by the name of Vanderpool, set up the world's first practical street railway. Horse cars had, of course, been drawn on rails for years, and electric systems had been tried – but heavy rains or snow would invariably short-circuit the power rail buried in the ground.

Wright's solution was the electric trolley pole. He carried his electricity

The bubbles that saved Ontario a million dollars

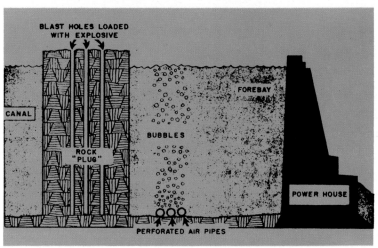

It took six tons of dynamite to blast out 25,000 tons of rock wedged between two adjacent power plants at Adam Beck Generating Station . . . and a great deal of ingenuity. The problem facing Ontario Hydro engineers: how to release the explosion without damaging a powerhouse only 85 yards away. One solution would have been to close down the generator and drain out the main forebay, but this would have cost $1 million. Adolphe J. Laprairie came up with the answer, by installing perforated air pipes that created a wall of bubbles between the power house and the rock, to cushion equipment from the blast.

The first meal cooked with electric power was prepared on apparatus provided by Thomas Ahearne at an Ottawa hotel.

in overhead wires, and brought it to the moving car through a trolley pole equipped with a wheel to reduce friction. This system, built in 1883 and improved in 1884, was tried out at the Canadian National Exhibition. Thousands went for a pioneering ride, and the experimental electric trolley more than proved itself, running well in rain or shine, with no breakdowns. Wright's basic system quickly spread to all major cities of the world.

In 1892 Thomas Ahearne, of Ottawa, made streetcar travel comfortable with his invention of an electrical car-heating system. This made year-round streetcar service possible for the first time in severe climates. Ahearne also invented an electric sweeper for removing snow from the streetcar tracks and switch points.

The Pogue carburetor

The one invention that almost every Canadian knows a little about – if only a garbled rumour – is the Pogue carburetor. The carburetor that gives 100 to 200 miles on a

The man who made the streetcar work

J. J. Wright was the electrical wizard of his day. He built the first electric railway, devised the trolley pole system, installed Canada's first electric motor, and brightened the streets of Toronto, equipping the city with its first arc lamps.

A cross section of a streetcar, showing Ahearne's electric boilers: they took the chill out of Canada's winter transit.

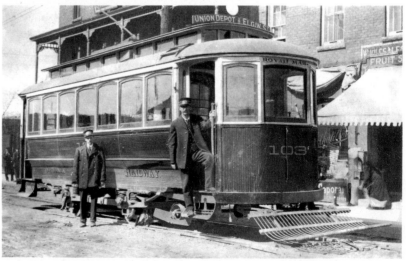

Overhead wires may be an eyesore, but Wright's trolley pole system made street railways dependable for the first time. This oldtimer operated in Ottawa.

A major invention – the overhead power system for streetcars – was demonstrated at the C.N.E. in 1883. These passengers rode Canada's first electric railway.

The trolley-bus was a natural development from the electric street railway. It was powered by overhead wires, but eliminated the need for expensive tracks.

Winnipeg Free Press

WINNIPEG, FRIDAY, AUGUST 14, 1936.　　Forecast—CLOUDY; SHOWERS

Carburetor Invention Stolen

Their Invention Stolen by Thugs

ITERS TO ...TH GOVT.

Thugs Raid C. N. Pogue's Workshop in Amphitheatre

Three Million-dollar Models of Device to Give Cars 200 Miles Per Gallon Are Stolen When Inventor Goes to Lunch

Inventor

Police, Friday, are conducting a city-wide hunt for three "million-dollar carburetors," stolen from the inventor's workshop in the Amphitheatre rink some time during the noon

Page one news, but some people alleged the burglary was faked, and that Pogue had sold out to the oil interests.

Nelson Pogue: a carburetor that could run a car 200 miles on a gallon of gas?

gallon of gasoline or, alternatively, the pill, which, dropped into a gasoline tank full of water, runs an automobile, are the hardy perennials of the invention world. Every few years the newspapers break out a new story of a magic carburetor.

The *locus classicus* of all carburetor stories is that of Nelson Pogue, of Winnipeg. About 1938 Pogue conceived the idea (probably not original with him) of forcing the air-fuel mixture into the engine through a long spiral baffle, rather than directly into the engine manifold as was the usual case. This spiral baffle was heated by exhaust gases, and gave up its heat to the fuel-air mixture. Thus, according to Pogue, by the time it got to be burned in the engine cylinder, the gas was in a state to give up most of its energy for the production of power, rather than having most of its energy wasted. Citizens of Winnipeg still swear that Pogue demonstrated the carburetor in his car on the road to Winnipeg Beach time after time, and that it did produce something like 200 miles to the gallon. Some say that Pogue's carburetor failed, not because it couldn't produce the mileage, but because it had the bad habit of burning out engines.

Other people look for more sinister forces. Many believe, even today, that Pogue was bought off by the oil companies. Some of my eager informants were able to give me the exact amount, $1 million, and the name of the oil company that gave it to him. Moreover, they cite the "cover story" that was worked out to cover the bribe.

Pogue had a workshop, so the story goes, in the old Winnipeg amphi-

theatre rink which had been given him free of charge by one of his backers, W. Holmes. In August, 1936 a skylight over this workshop was broken and all Pogue's papers, models and records were stolen. People "in the know" saw immediately that this was a faked burglary. The Chief of Police himself said he thought it was an inside job and the police were not going to get involved.

Actually, the oil companies would like nothing better than to find an inventor who would show them how to get ten times the power out of a given unit of fuel. This would mean that airplanes could carry more payload and less fuel, and would vastly increase the efficiency of every type of powered vehicle. It is more likely an oil company would pay a million dollars to *develop* such an invention rather than a million dollars to suppress it.

One Canadian invention that certainly *did* stand up in the internal-combustion engine field was the sleeve valve, developed by Tom McCollum, of Toronto. It provided a way of getting around the problem of over-heating of exhaust valves which had plagued aircraft-engine designers for twenty years. Sleeve-valve engines were used in many aircraft in World War II. They were finally eliminated by the sodium exhaust valve which combined rapid heat dissipation with poppet-valve efficiency.

Energy from the atom

Canada has an honourable place in the succession of world scientists and experimenters who, since the turn of the century, have unlocked the secrets of the atom and given us the mighty genie of atomic power. Only two years after the French physicist Antoine Becquerel had noticed the first evidence of radioactivity, the New Zealander Ernest Rutherford was beginning his research studies at McGill University, Montreal. With the English-born chemist Frederick Soddy, Rutherford worked out, between 1898 and 1902, a theory of the spontaneous disintegration of the atom, and studied all the then-known radioactive elements. During Rutherford's nine years as Professor of Physics at McGill, one of his students was Otto Hahn, who in 1938, back in Germany, studied the bombardment of uranium by neutrons and laid the groundwork for the release of atomic energy.

Canada was an ideal place for research on atomic energy. It is one of the few places in the world blessed with abundant natural raw materials. In 1930, Gilbert LaBine and Charles St. Paul discovered a large deposit of pitchblende, the ore of radium, on the shores of Great Bear Lake and, by the end of the decade, the output of the Eldorado Mine had made Canada one of two world suppliers of radium.

When World War II began, the National Research Council in Ottawa had a small group under George C. Lawrence working in nuclear physics. Early in 1940, working with W. B. Sergeant of Queen's University, the group set up experiments to test the possibility of nuclear fission. A ton of uranium 238 was borrowed from Eldorado Mining & Refining and, by year's end, a crude pile had been put together in a third-floor room of the N.R.C. building.

Gilbert LaBine on his historic prospecting expedition of 1930. With Charles St. Paul, he lugged 1,600 pounds of supplies on this sleigh for 200 miles, until on May 16, at Great Bear Lake, he discovered the pitchblende that pushed Canada into the atomic age.

This was the discovery vein of pitchblende which in 1930 launched the radium industry of Canada. LaBine (standing left) *found silver here, too, and copper so rich that he could carve his initials into it with a prospecting pick.*

By the late Thirties, this mining camp had sprung up alongside Echo Bay. When scientists began to develop the atomic bomb, the Crown took over the Eldorado Mine.

Eldorado, 1935: in winter, dog teams hauled out the pitchblende concentrates to freight planes landing on the frozen lake. The ore was refined into radium at Port Hope, Ont.

Information on the use of heavy water as a moderator arrived from Cambridge University and, by the end of 1940, an Allied team of British, U.S. and Canadian scientists was hard at work on the atomic bomb. The project was pushed forward in the U.S. on a massive scale and with characteristic energy. On December 2, 1942, in a squash court under the grandstand of Stagg Field, at the University of Chicago, the world's first chain reaction and production of atomic power took place.

In the summer of 1942, a joint U.K.-Canadian atomic research project was set up formally at the University of Montreal and, by the end of that year, had 340 people on its staff. It was decided to use heavy water, instead of carbon, as the moderator in the Canadian pile, and a site for the manufacture of heavy water had to be found. This finally turned out to be Chalk River, Ontario. In 1945 the pile-building process was moved from Montreal to Chalk River and, on September 5 of that year, the *Zeep*, the first atomic-energy reactor in Canada, and the first in the world outside the United States, began to produce power. Out of this wartime research came Canada's atomic industry, which is now playing an important role in the world.

The Cobalt 60 breakthrough

In the 1950s, the increasing power shortage in heavily industrialized southern Ontario made it seem feasible to use atomic power for electrical generation, even in a country endowed with vast resources for hydroelectric power. The N.P.D. reactor

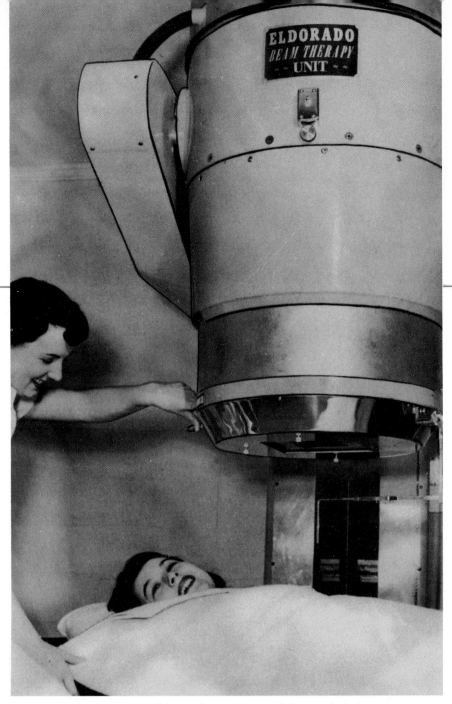

The "bomb" that saves lives: Eldorado Beam Therapy Units, popularly known as cobalt bombs, have brought the ray of hope to millions of cancer-sufferers the world over. Atomic Energy of Canada pioneered this field of cancer treatment in 1951.

came out of the preliminary studies, and the first large power station, called c.a.n.d.u. (Canadian Deuterium Uranium), was authorized with a planned production of 200,000 kilowatts of electricity. In co-operation with Ontario Hydro, the Douglas Point generating station was built on the shore of Lake Huron. It came into service in 1965. Two years later, Atomic Energy of Canada had five reactors in operation at Chalk River for research on various aspects of the use and control of atomic energy.

To the general public of the world the best-known aspect of Canada's work in atomic energy is the Cobalt 60 therapy unit which a.e.c.'s commercial products division has built and distributed. In the late Forties, it was realized that a method was needed to replace radium therapy for treating cancer. The first result of the group's research was the Eldorado A Cobalt 60 Therapy Unit. This was used in the London Clinic of the Ontario Cancer Foundation in the fall of 1951 – the first commercially produced equipment of its type in the world. Since then, Canadian cancer

therapy units have been much improved and are now in use in forty countries. One and a half million treatments a year are provided by these Canadian-built machines.

Canada has also developed the Gammacell, a portable irradiation unit designed for industrial research. A spectacular recent development of the a.e.c. group is the mobile Cobalt 60 irradiator. This is mounted on a large truck which can take it to agricultural districts. It was found that irradiation of potatoes, for example, vastly increased their storage life.

5 / DELVING THE EARTH
Riches from raw materials

Canada possesses one of the world's great treasure houses of raw materials and Canadian inventors have, accordingly, been pioneers in the techniques of mining, chemicals, metallurgy, and paper making. The first commercial oil well, the first oil pipeline, the first commercial acetylene, the first wood pulp mill in North America all resulted from the work of Canadians.

One of the greatest of these pioneers was Thomas L. Willson who was trying to make diamonds in Hamilton, Ontario, in the late 19th century. He failed at that but he did later invent the process for making carbide and acetylene and became known as "Carbide" Willson. From his discoveries grew the giant Union Carbide Company in the United States and the Shawinigan Chemical Company of Canada.

Born at Woodstock in 1861, Willson moved to Hamilton and experimented with electrodynamos when he was only 15 years old. He turned his attention to the electric arc furnace and finally became interested in the aluminum industry.

In the 1880s, the expensive Castner process involving the use of sodium for making aluminum was the best available. Willson, who needed only a hint to get started on a new process, realized that if sodium could be used so could calcium, and a calcium process would be much cheaper. Accordingly, he tried to make calcium by reducing lime with coke in an electric furnace. By this time Willson had taken his talents to the United States, and was experimenting with electric furnaces in New Jersey.

Early in 1892 one of his arc furnace experiments produced a strange crystalline material. When a pebble of this new stuff was dropped into water, instead of vigorously producing hydrogen gas – as did sodium – the new material reacted quietly, producing a gas which burned with a smoky flame. Clearly it was a hydrocarbon.

Willson wrote to Lord Kelvin at Glasgow University (one of the great

"Carbide" Willson's development of acetylene made possible the oxy-acetylene torch, a welding and metal-cutting tool which proved invaluable in ship and car production.

Acetylene lit the streets of Maxville, Ont., until electricity snuffed it out.

brains of the day) to discuss what he had produced. The substance turned out to be carbide and the gas acetylene, the source of a large number of important chemicals. Willson was not the first to study the properties of carbide, but he was the first to produce large enough quantities to make it available on a commercial scale. He sold his process and patents to the Union Carbide Company and, in 1896, returned to Canada to set up his own carbide and acetylene works at Merritton, near St. Catharines, Ontario.

By the turn of the century, major cities already had electric power. The path of development at that time seemed to be to build power sites remote from the cities, and then attract industries to these sites with cheap electricity. Canada's first venture of this kind was the Shawinigan Water & Power Company, organized in 1897 to harness the St. Maurice River, at Shawinigan Falls, Quebec. Among the industries set up to use the cheap power was the Shawinigan Carbide Company, and Thomas Willson, as the chief North American authority on carbide and acetylene, was brought in as vice-president.

To light the streets

It was still anybody's guess which source of power would turn out in the long run to be best for street lighting: acetylene gas, coal gas, kerosene or electricity. The situation was further complicated by a radically new invention. Gaslight offered only a soft and yellow flame, and the strong white light of the electric arc would soon have put it out of business. But

then the German von Welsbach invented the gas burner mantle: a piece of cloth impregnated with the oxides of rare metals such as cerium. When a normal gas flame was burned on this mantle, the light became whiter and many times brighter. Gas was back in the bidding.

At Shawinigan, "Carbide" Willson quickly gathered around him ingenious men to put up a good fight for the lucrative street-lighting business. One of these was A. MacMillan who concentrated on the invention of carbon generators to produce the highly saleable carbon black. In the lighting field, Willson was fortunate in attracting E. A. LeSueur. One of the big problems in using acetylene for street lighting is that the gas is bulky and explosive when liquefied. Le-Sueur in 1903 conceived the brilliant idea of solidifying acetylene gas by means of extreme cold, and then shipping it in insulated containers. This system was used by the town of Maxville, Ontario, for several years. Eventually, however, because of improvements in incandescent bulbs, the switch from DC to AC, and improved electrical distribution systems, the street-lighting competition was won by electricity.

Willson's acetylene had, by this time, found its most important use. The oxy-acetylene torch was invented in 1903 and quickly caught on. It gave a temperature of 6,000° Fahrenheit, hot enough not only to serve for welding but as a fast and cheap cutting torch for thick plates of steel. Willson's search for a new way of making aluminum in the 1880s thus ended in the early 1900s with the oxy-acetylene torch, the device that

This advertisement in the London Free Press *in 1859 is believed to be the first to promote carbon oil produced from Canadian petroleum.*

WHEN BLACK GOLD STARTED A BOOM

In 1857 oil was discovered at Enniskillen, Canada West, and soon inventive Canadian engineers were developing their own rigs and gear. A new industry was born.

The Scientific American.

The Coal Oil in Canada.

MESSRS. EDITORS:—I have just returned from our new oil diggings on Black creek, in the township of Enniskillen, county of Lambton, Canada West. I found them very prolific. In one locality as the creek, within the distance of 1½ miles, there has been, and is being sunk, since last March, some 100 *surface* and *rock* wells, not one of which has as yet, when completed, failed to afford a good supply of oil; and hundreds more will be sunk in the immediate vicinity of these between now and fall. Those now there from the Pennsylvania, Virginia and Ohio wells, and they are not a few in number, say that our Enniskillen oil diggings are far more promising than any yet discovered in the United States, and that the oil, both surface and rock, is of a superior quality. And, on experiment, it proves to be a desirable oil for the lubrication of machinery, even in its crude state. One engineer of 14 years' experience running an engine for pumping purposes remarked to me that he was using it wholly, and that it was superior to any oil he had ever yet used. But there is one thing much needed there immediately, viz., good barrel machinery to be run with steam. They cannot get barrels to put their oil in, consequently are obliged to build tanks to hold it for the present. It is a fine opening for the running of good barrel machinery, and there is plenty of good oak timber; also for the sale of small portable engines and good pumps.

At a place called Petrolia, on Bear creek, a few miles from the above-mentioned locality, where there are a number of wells in successful operation, a Boston company are erecting a refinery, (now nearly completed,) of sufficient capacity to refine 90 barrels a day. Others should be erected on Black creek, that they might thereby send to market nothing but the pure article for illumination or lubrication It would make a saving in both barrels and transportation; although from tests made with this oil in Cleveland and Detroit they pronounce the waste to be only 15 per cent in refining—85 per cent burning fluid, and the balance good for other purposes.

Having no speculative interest in this matter whatever, I have made the above statement in sincerity and truth.   C. B. THOMSON.

St. Catharines, C. W., June 27, 1861.

System of Filing Papers

MESSRS. EDITORS—I have a system of filing papers, particularly the SCIENTIFIC AMERICAN, which I desire to communicate to my fellow readers. Here is the system: In a drawer in my reading room I have arranged a low box with partitions, each partition being designed to hold one volume. When I am done reading the paper *pro tem* I fold it once and place it in the box, relatively to the preceding or subsequent number. By observing this rule as often as I take a paper from the box I am enabled to separate any one from the rest in a minute's time.

SUBSCRIBER.

Mechanicsburg, Ohio, July 3, 1861.

Sawyer's Projectile

MESSRS EDITORS—I am, as you suppose, familiar with Sawyer's shot, and personally acquainted with ...

directly to one of the judges, from such decision of the Commissioner. Not so under the new law of 1861. The primary Examiner and the Examiners-in-Chief are all, by the act of 1861, treated as judicial officers, having power, without control, within the sphere of their duty, to the exercise of their independent judgment. Their acts, under the new law are not, as under the old system, the acts of the Commissioner, but their own acts. They are no longer the mere organs of the Commissioner, but independent ...

Above: Canadian oil was far better than Yankee stuff, a St. Catharines writer boasted to a U.S. publication in June, 1861.

DUNDAS IRON FOUNDRY

AND

MACHINE SHOP,

ESTABLISHED IN 1838.

JOHN GARTSHORE,

MANUFACTURER OF

STEAM ENGINES, BOILERS,

MILL MACHINERY OF ALL KINDS,

Oil Stills, Tanks, Car Wheels & Locomotive Castings,

GARTSHORE'S TREBLE SUCTION SMUT MACHINES,

LOAM, DRY SAND AND GREEN SAND CASTINGS, OF EVERY DESCRIPTION, AND ANY WEIGHT.

PORTABLE MILLS, MILL STONES, WATER WHEELS, BRAN DUSTERS, SEPARATORS, &c. &c. &c.

One industry spurs another. Many machines used at the Ontario oil fields were made at Dundas, as suggested by this ad of 1862.

THE CANADIAN COAL OIL COMPANY employ sixteen men, and turn out about 120 barrels of oil per week. The machinery used in the refining process cost $22,000. A capital of $56,000 is invested in the business. The refinery, situated outside the corporation, on the line of the G. W. R., has been in operation about three years. The Canadian Oil Company manufacture illuminating and machine oil, and naptha. All the raw oil is procured from the Enniskillen oil wells. Since a duty of ten per cent has been placed on all imported oils, it is more than probable the home article will be used exclusively.

THE HAMILTON OIL COMPANY was organized in October, 1861, with a capital of $40,000. They employ ten men, besides others indirectly. At present they turn out 100 barrels per week; in the course of two months they expect to manufacture 150 bbls per week. All the raw material is procured in Enniskillen, where the Company owns 100 acres of oil land, containing ten surface wells. Hitherto the greatest difficulty has been the want of a steady market, but arrangements have been completed to supply foreign demand. Present price of burning oil 25c per gallon.

Right: Industrial promotion, vintage 1862. Both notices appeared in the Commercial Directory *for Hamilton, Canada West.*

From a lump of coal, Dr. Abraham Gesner distilled a fuel called kerosene, and lit the way for North America's oil refining industry.

played a key role in the fabrication of all metals but, especially, in the shipbuilding and automobile industries.

The transportation industry as we know it today would not exist had it not been for Willson's commercial production of "the gas that burned with a smoky flame."

The grandfather of oil

When Provincial Geologist Dr. Abraham Gesner was fired by a parsimonious New Brunswick Government in 1842, he set up Canada's first museum and then, tired of the smoky lamps of the period, he distilled a fluid from coal which he named kerosene. He was thus in effect, the grandfather of the North American petroleum industry.

One of the most remarkable Canadians of all time, Gesner was born at Cornwallis in 1797. He took a medical degree, married, and settled down as a country doctor but his true love was geology. In 1836 he published *The Geology and Mineralogy of Nova Scotia*, and two years later New Brunswick appointed him Provincial Geologist. For four happy years Gesner roamed the province by canoe and on foot, locating most of the mineral deposits which have since made New Brunswick an important mining area, and gathering in the process a unique collection of mineral samples.

When his natural history museum did not prosper, Gesner began to experiment in lighting materials. Whale oil and other animal and vegetable oils that had been used for centuries were both smoky and smelly;

they also produced a feeble light. Tallow candles were always in short supply and expensive.

In 1846 Gesner gave a public demonstration in a church hall in Charlottetown, Prince Edward Island. He set up distillation equipment, put a few lumps of coal into it and heated the retort. When a few ounces of a clear fluid had been distilled, he poured it into an oil lamp and struck his phosphorus match to the wick. According to contemporary accounts, the room was filled with a beautiful yellow glow which eclipsed the smoky flame of the whale-oil lamps. Gesner returned in triumph to Halifax where he organized his Kerosene Gaslight Company to light the homes and streets of Halifax.

Like so many other Canadian inventors, Gesner moved to the United States where his patents were used to found the North America Gaslight Company, at Hunter's Point, New York. The oil produced by Gesner's process had one bad feature – a disgusting odour. But the light it produced was very bright, and this was the main consideration. At age 65 he was able to retire to Halifax, a wealthy man. The New York company he founded eventually became part of the Standard Oil Company of New Jersey, owner of Imperial Oil of Canada.

Black gold from Black Creek

The first oil company in North America was founded by Charles N. Tripp, of Woodstock, Ontario. It happened this way: The chief chemist of the Geological Survey of Canada, Thomas Hunt, reported in 1849 that

asphalt found in Enniskillen Township contained 78 to 81 per cent combustible and volatile matter. Sir William Logan, the Provincial Geologist, sent his assistant, Alexander Murray, to Enniskillen to look at the deposits more carefully. Murray lived near Woodstock, and was a neighbour of the Tripp brothers, Charles and Henry. It is probable that Tripp's idea of founding an oil company was based on the best geological studies of the time.

Charles Tripp applied for a charter to the Legislative Council of Upper Canada in 1852 and, in the same year, began to erect buildings and machinery for the manufacture of asphalt. The first petition was refused and it was not until 1854 that the International Mining and Manufacturing Company received its official charter. This was just two weeks before the Pennsylvania Rock Oil Company – the first oil company in the United States – received its charter. Tripp was actually producing asphalt before the official charter was granted to his company. A sample of his product, which he sent to the Universal Exhibition in Paris in 1855, won an Honorable Mention.

Lack of capital, and transportation problems, proved too much for Tripp and the assets of his company were taken over by James Miller Williams, of Hamilton. Williams had built and sold a successful carriage business and then had built the first cars to run west of Toronto on the Great Western Railway.

An experienced businessman, Williams was to prove the true father of the North American oil industry. There is some evidence that he knew

James Miller Williams (shown with his wife) *dug the 65-foot hole near Oil Springs, Ontario, that in 1857 became the first commercial oil well in North America.*

Remains of an old well at Oil Springs, Ontario. Near here, Canada's first refinery was built, but the oil boom was eclipsed by the discovery of richer fields at Petrolia. Deep-drilling in 1881 (note more modern rig in background) pumped a new prosperity into the area.

Over the soft soil surrounding Petrolia and Oil Springs, planked toll roads were built to haul wagonloads of oil to the railway.

At Wyoming, Ontario, oil barrels were loaded onto the Great Western Railway and lugged to the head of Lake Ontario.

Big Bear Creek offered an alternate route. Barrels of oil were floated to the St. Clair River, and hauled aboard ships, 1862.

Abraham Gesner and, if so, this would account for his extensive technical knowledge. Williams was the first man to dig for oil and the first to find it in commercial quantities sufficient to justify building a refinery.

In 1857 Williams, with Tripp as his employee, dug a well near Bothwell, on the banks of the Thames River. When they reached 27 feet the hole filled with oil and water, and the well was abandoned when they ran into difficulties trying to go deeper. The same year they moved to the Enniskillen area, near Black Creek, and dug a well 65 feet deep. This one was an immediate success and between five and 100 barrels of oil a day were taken from it. The first oil refinery in Canada was built by Williams the same year to use the product of the Enniskillen well.

The founders of the Pennsylvania Rock Oil Company had also run into financial difficulties and had been taken over by a group of Connecticut investors. They reincorporated as the Seneca Oil Company in 1858, and hired Edwin L. Drake to drill for oil. A Pittsburgh chemist, Dr. H. C. Tweedell, Drake's chief rival, determined to find oil for himself before Drake did. Studying geological reports of oil seepages, he came across two at Dover, New Brunswick, that looked promising.

Early in 1859, while Drake was still drilling without success near Titusville, Pennsylvania, Tweedell arrived at Dover, hired workmen and oxen, and began to drill. By midsummer he had punch-drilled four wells, the deepest down to 190 feet, and he had hit both gas and oil. His wells threatened to flood with water, but he was nevertheless very optimistic. But on August 28, he got a telegram saying that Drake had struck oil at Titusville at a depth of only 69 feet, and that the well was producing 25 barrels a day. Everybody thought there was room in North America for only one producing oil well, so the disappointed Tweedell closed up shop.

A gusher at Petrolia

These wells, drilled in Canada in the summer of 1859, have been called the first *drilled* wells in North America, but this is probably not true. While specific evidence is hard to come by, James Miller Williams' well No. 27 was described in 1861 by a correspondent of the Toronto *Globe* as having been in operation "over two years." This well was dug 46 feet to the rock, and then bored another 100 feet. It produced the then-astonishing total of 60 barrels a day. The correspondent's dating would place this producing well in the summer of 1859, and thus *before* the Drake well at Titusville. Moreover, this well was named No. 27, indicating that Williams, a meticulous businessman, probably had 26 previous wells. Thus it seems reasonable to suppose that Williams had drilled several wells between his first unsuccessful attempt at Bothwell in the summer of 1857, and the successful No. 27 in 1859.

When the Drake well came in, there was a tremendous oil boom in the United States and the Canadian industry went into a temporary decline. This was largely because the American lamp oil had a lower sulphur content, hence was not as smelly as the Canadian brand. But in January 1862, Ontario had its own oil boom when John Shaw, an itinerant photographer of whom very little is known, operated a foot power rig to drive a well near Petrolia. At 160 feet he struck a gusher, which ran uncontrolled for a week and covered the clay soil with a layer of oil a foot deep. It even left a greasy deposit on the waters of nearby Lake St. Clair.

The first oil pipeline in North America was built from Petrolia to Sarnia in the early 1860s. Natives of the oil-producing district of Ontario claim that the jerker rod system was invented there. This is a system of linked poles which are made to oscillate by a single power source, thus carrying the power to widely separated wells. The earlier systems employed steam power and as many as 200 wells were pumped by one engine.

J. H. Fairbanks, one of the founders of Petrolia and a pioneer in the Canadian oil industry, is credited as inventor of this system. He testified before a Royal Commission on Mineral Resources that he had first used the system in 1863. The jerker rod system is still used in the Oil Springs district. Nowadays, up to twenty wells are operated from one engine house with an electric motor.

One of the most striking examples of ingenuity by a Canadian oil man in a crisis was that exhibited by V. J. "Tip" Monroney, an executive of Imperial Oil at Calgary. After the Leduc Field, south of Edmonton, was discovered in 1947, many oil companies began drilling in the area. In 1948, Atlantic No. 3 well came in as

A big problem called for unconventional thinking. V. J. Monroney plugged a runaway gusher with chicken wire and burlap.

This forest of oil wells made Petrolia, originally called Enniskillen, the oil capital of Canada in the 1860s. Canadian Oil Co. Ltd. and Imperial Oil Co. built refineries here, although Imperial moved to Sarnia in 1899, pumping crude from Petrolia by pipeline.

a gusher and went wild, blowing off 200 million cubic feet of gas and between 8,000 and 16,000 barrels of crude oil a day. When it finally caught fire, the flames rose 1,100 feet, and could be seen for fifty miles.

The problem was, first, to get the fire out, and then to control the flow of gas and oil from the well. Many conventional methods were tried and oil-fire experts were brought in from as far away as Texas. They got the fire out, but the well was still flowing uncontrolled at such a rate that owners of neighbouring properties were beginning to wonder if it would drain their holdings. The runaway gusher was taken over by the Province of Alberta Conservation Board, and Monroney was brought in on loan

from Imperial Oil to control it.

At first, his team, working day and night, tried conventional methods, and eventually had two holes drilled down to the source of the oil, angled in from either side. The second drill actually hit the original hole several thousand feet down. But the trouble was, the immense pressure and flow had produced a tremendous underground cavern. How big that cavern was is indicated by the fact that 14,000 pounds of sawdust and shavings, a couple of boxcars of turkey feathers mixed with mud, 4,000 cubic feet of zonolite (an insulator), several carloads of sugarcane fibres, 2,000 bags of Gyproc (a quick-setting cement), and other assorted materials were poured into the cavern without

visible effect. Finally, they pumped in an entire trainload of cement, but still the gusher continued to erupt.

Monroney then had to take a less conventional look at the problem. He decided they were dealing with something like an underground church with a very tall steeple. The church body was the underground cavern and the steeple the original drill hole. The only way to stop the flow of gas and oil would be somehow to put a plug in the steeple, rather than trying to fill up the whole church.

Once the concept was clear, Monroney lost no time inventing his "bazooka". It was a device made of burlap and one-inch-mesh chicken wire rolled together and stuffed into

65

When an oil well goes wild, it can transform a fountain of black gold into a raging pillar of fire. The giant blowtorch that rose from Atlantic No. 3 at the Leduc field in Alberta in 1948 was extinguished, and Canadian inventiveness found the way to cap the gusher.

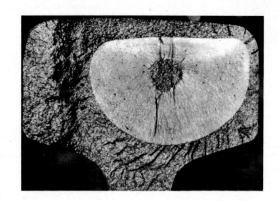

Minute interior cracks in moulded steel rails caused serious accidents until a young N.S. metallurgist solved the problem.

a standard 32-foot length of five-inch drilling tube. This was dropped down the well and exploded at the point where the steeple section began to expand into the church itself. The springiness of the chicken wire and the burlap combined to block off the runaway well long enough to permit something heavier to be dropped down.

Once the main flow was blocked off, fifty bags of cement and calcium chloride were dropped in, and finally cement was pushed in under 36,000 pounds pressure. By the ingenious means of the "bazooka", designed under the spur of necessity, a multi-million-dollar well was finally brought under control.

Cameron Mackie's wonder rail

One of the mysteries of steel fabrication was the internal cracking in seemingly perfect new rails. This was first demonstrated in the laboratories of the Pennsylvania Railroad in 1918. The upper half of the railhead was removed by sawing or planing, and the resulting flat surface etched with strong acid. The acid revealed previously invisible fissures, proving that the rail was defective even though no outside evidence of imperfection could be seen.

For some years afterwards, there was a heated debate between rail manufacturers and railroad engineers as to whether the internal cracks were the cause of rails breaking in service. The most important type of breakage, where the rail broke completely in half – often causing a bad accident – was the type known as transverse fissure. At the point where

the break took place, a smooth oval area could usually be seen. This proved that the rail had failed progressively, beginning with a small crack, but finally covering almost the entire railhead at the point of breakage. The nature of the transverse fissure, when it was understood, led to two approaches to solving the problem.

The first was based on the discovery that the transverse fissure in a rail led to a change in its magnetic or electrical properties. This change could be detected by an instrument passing over the rail. Out of this came the Sperry car, a specially-built rolling laboratory which would test the rail as it passed.

The second, and in the long run more practical, approach was to assume that a rail that showed minute cracks when first manufactured would in time develop transverse and other fissures because of the pounding of locomotive wheels. The problem resolved itself into the question of deciding at what stage in the rail-making process the tiny cracks were produced.

About 1930 this problem was brought to the attention of J. Cameron Mackie, a young metallurgist at the plant of Dominion Steel & Coal Corporation at Sydney, Nova Scotia. He discovered almost immediately that the cracks were not a high-temperature phenomenon, as had been thought previously, but were forming in the rails at a relatively low temperature. He then found that if the cooling of rails could be slowed, the cracks could be entirely eliminated without softening the rails. After this, it was just a matter of working

out the best commercial practice for retarded cooling, determining the best cooling rates and times, before commercial production could begin. The world's first production of shatter-free rails took place at Sydney in July, 1931, when 4,500 tons were rolled for the C.P.R.

Mackie's method of retarding and controlling the cooling process was very simple. After forming, the rails were allowed to cool naturally on the mill cooling beds until just after they ceased glowing red hot. They were then lifted into huge steel boxes, stacked until the box was full with 120 rails, and a heavy cover put on to shield them from drafts. Twenty-four hours later the entire batch had cooled to within 100° Fahrenheit of normal room temperature.

Exhaustive tests on etched rail samples showed that identical steel formulas and heats would produce fissures if cooled normally, and would never produce fissures if cooled according to the Mackie process. By 1933 the only other rail mill in Canada, Algoma Steel's, was using the Mackie process under license.

Mackie's patent was granted in Canada in February 1932. Thereafter the system was patented in most of the major countries of the world, including the United States. Bethlehem Steel in the U.S. began litigation against the patent, but later changed its mind and paid royalties to Mackie for many years. By World War II all U.S. rail mills were using the Mackie system, either with or without payment of royalties, and most rails made throughout the world used controlled cooling as envisaged by the Sydney inventor.

Turning trees into paper

Canada's largest export industry, the manufacture of pulp and paper, got off to a slow and uncertain start. The first papermaker seems to have been Brown of Lower Canada, who was advertising handmade rag papers in 1805. About the same time the first paper mill in Canada was built by a group of New Englanders at St. Andrews East, Quebec. A quarter of a century later, there were paper mills in both Upper and Lower Canada. In 1831, John McLenehan and Company were advertising in the Montreal *Gazette* that their mill was in operation. At Belleville, they offered straw paper and other types of wrapping paper, and also newsprint. By 1846, there were five or six paper mills in Canada West and at least three in Quebec – at Port Neuf, Chambly and Stanstead. The first Canadian patents for paper-making are Nos. 470 and 550 granted, respectively, to Andres and Taylor in 1854 and 1855.

Many Maritimers believe that Charles Fenerty, of Halifax, is an inventor of world significance because he discovered the process of making paper from wood fibre. In 1838, almost two decades before the European process of making newsprint from wood pulp was invented, Fenerty claimed to have demonstrated a usable newsprint which he had made from wood.

The American Civil War caused a great shortage of rags and cloth, and, since paper was normally made from rags, there was a consequent shortage of paper. John Thompson, of Napanee, Ontario, applied his mind to finding a substitute and, in the early

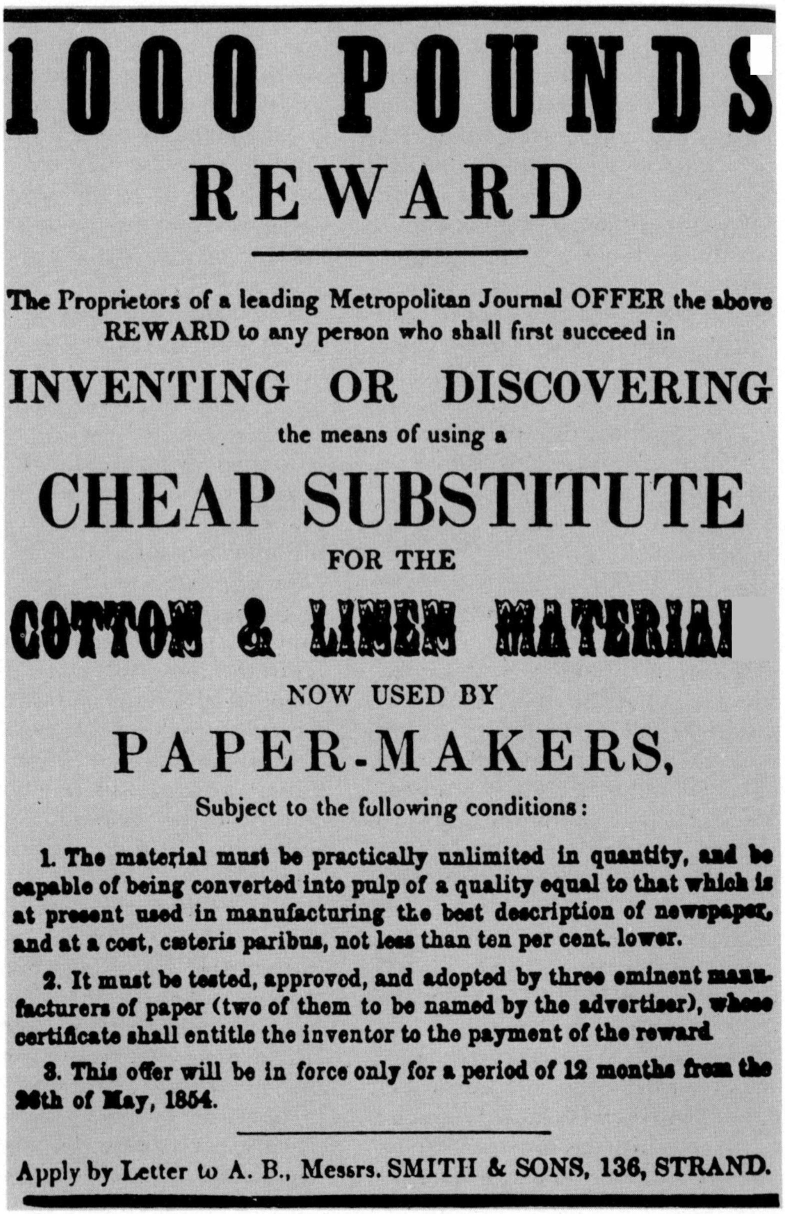

1000 POUNDS

REWARD

The Proprietors of a leading Metropolitan Journal OFFER the above REWARD to any person who shall first succeed in

INVENTING OR DISCOVERING

the means of using a

CHEAP SUBSTITUTE

FOR THE

COTTON & LINEN MATERIAL

NOW USED BY

PAPER-MAKERS,

Subject to the following conditions:

1. The material must be practically unlimited in quantity, and be capable of being converted into pulp of a quality equal to that which is at present used in manufacturing the best description of newspaper, and at a cost, cæteris paribus, not less than ten per cent. lower.

2. It must be tested, approved, and adopted by three eminent manufacturers of paper (two of them to be named by the advertiser), whose certificate shall entitle the inventor to the payment of the reward.

3. This offer will be in force only for a period of 12 months from the 26th of May, 1854.

Apply by Letter to A. B., Messrs. SMITH & SONS, 136, STRAND.

The search for a cheap method of paper manufacture was world-wide and desperate, as reflected by this 1854 advertisement. Twelve years later, North America's first commercial wood pulp was mechanically produced in Quebec.

This sawing machine, which appeared in the Canadian Illustrated News *in 1862, was "capable of cutting 60 cords of wood per day." Mechanization helped make forest products a leading industry in Canada.*

1860s, was one of the first men in the world – and certainly the first in North America – to demonstrate that paper could be made from wood pulp. Alex Buntin, in 1866, prepared the first commercial mechanical pulp in North America, in a groundwood mill set up at Valleyfield, Quebec, just west of Montreal.

Toward the end of the 19th century, the Canadian pulp and paper industry grew spectacularly. As daily newspapers became popular in the large cities of the United States, the demand for newsprint spiralled. The Chicago *Tribune*, to ensure a continuous supply of newsprint, set up plants at Thorold, Ontario, and later at Baie Comeau, Quebec. Other American newspapers made long-term contracts which permitted Canadian paper companies to make the large capital investment which was required in order to produce newsprint in large quantities.

The first plant in North America to manufacture kraft paper was that of the Brompton (Quebec) Pulp & Paper Company, at East Angus, in 1907. Kraft paper, which is used for wrapping and for making packing boxes and cardboard boxes, gets its name from the German word *kraft*, which means "strong." More varieties of wood can be used in this process – a very important factor to Canadian foresters.

Canadian pulp and paper scientists have invented many improvements of the kraft process. A group at the Brown Corporation plant, at Latuque, Quebec, in 1915 worked out a process for burning the concentrated fluid (called "black liquor"), that is a by-product of the process. In 1926 this development was carried an important step farther by John H. Tomlinson Jr., of Howard Smith Paper Mills, resulting in a black-liquor furnace for kraft mills, of a design which is now used all over the world.

Two great names in the Canadian pulp industry are Charles and John Riordon. Their company was well established at Merritton, Ontario, supplying rag paper, when in 1890 it bought the rights to the German process for boiling shredded wood in sulphite and "digesting" it under steam pressure. Two digesters were installed at Merritton. During World War I there was a shortage of cotton and the Riordon company began studies of the use of wood pulp for making viscose.

In 1920 the first bleached pulp of a special nature suitable for manufacture of rayon was produced. The constant demand for whiter and brighter paper, as well as the special needs of the rayon industry, in time produced new and better bleaching processes. The one developed by Dr. C. B. Thorne, of the International Paper Company (which had absorbed the Riordon Company in 1925), is now widely used.

During the Depression of the Thirties, the research department of the Howard Smith company, at Beauharnois, Quebec, worked out a process for extracting vanilin from waste sulfite cooking liquor. After World War II, the same company worked out a method of extracting lignin from soda pulp waste liquor. This material is used in paper-based laminates which are made by the company's subsidiary, Arborite Company Ltd., in Montreal.

How to look inside paper

The question of quality control on paper machines exercised Canadian scientists for sixty years, and, with the increase of rotary press speeds and the demand for higher quality, the problem became critical. The leading company in the application of sophisticated automatic control techniques to the pulp and paper industry has been Electronic Associates of Canada Ltd., of Toronto. In 1949, they began the development – in co-operation with the Pulp and Paper Research Institute of Canada – of an automatic instrument for measuring the amount of dirt in newsprint. By 1960 the company could read the actual fibre structure of a paper sample.

Another Canadian company, Isotope Products, of Oakville, Ontario, invented radiation devices for measuring the properties of paper, and the *Aquatel* for measuring the moisture content of the paper continuously.

In 1963, Isotope Products, which had previously been acquired by the Curtiss-Wright Corporation, was bought by Electronic Associates. They now have a completely automatic system which both measures and controls all the major factors which determine the quality of finished paper. These include caliper measurement for uniform thickness, determination of moisture content, holes, dirt and other flaws, brightness, finish and other properties.

Another company working in the field of quality control for the paper industry is Nash & Harrison Ltd., of Ottawa. Paul Nash holds patents on

Billions of Canada's trees – balsam, hemlock and spruce – have been rafted along the rivers, to be ground and cooked into pulp for the manufacture of newsprint and other papers. Above, two river drivers of the past century ride a timber slide at Ottawa

an optical detection machine for sheet materials such as paper. This machine has been sold chiefly to five paper manufacturers in England and in Europe. One Nash & Harrison machine replaces twenty girls in a sorting operation. Yet another Canadian, Elie Cowan, of Montreal, the inventor of the Cowan screen and several other machines for processing pulp and paper, has had a long history of supplying products to the industry.

By 1890, paper-making was highly mechanized. This was Joseph Ford's mill in Quebec.

AN
ALBUM
OF FORGOTTEN
CANADIAN
INVENTORS

JOHN MOLSON

John Molson arrived in Montreal from England in 1782, the first of a dynasty of bankers and brewers, a family that would do much to make Montreal one of the great cities of North America. He began with a small brewery at the foot of St. Mary's Current in Montreal harbour, and in 1809 introduced steam navigation on the St. Lawrence River, in the shape of the 85-foot paddle-wheeler Accommodation, the first steamship built entirely in North America. Riding with her on her maiden voyage from Montreal to Quebec on November 1 was Molson's hope for a regular steamship service. It took the Accommodation 36 running hours to reach Quebec — downstream — and an additional 30 hours at anchor, but Molson quickly built a second flagship, the longer and more powerful Swiftsure, first steamship to carry troops in Canada. The Malsham, Car of Commerce, and Lady Sherbrooke soon joined Molson's line, and it was not long before other company steamboats became common on the St. Lawrence, the Ottawa River, and the Great Lakes. John Molson's little Accommodation had carried Canada into the age of the steamship.

THOMAS L. WILLSON

*Even as a teen-ager in Hamilton, Ontario, Thomas
L. Willson delighted in tinkering with electric gadgets
and gimcracks, and ambitiously even tried his hand at
alchemy, hoping to convert the soot-black of carbon to
the sparkle of diamonds. Collaborating with a Hamilton
blacksmith, he constructed one of Canada's first
dynamos, and with it, produced that city's first arc light.
Like so many other important discoveries, Willson's
development of carbide and acetylene years later, in
1892, was the result of an accident, the byproduct of
another experiment. He was conducting an experiment
with an electric furnace, seeking a new process for
manufacturing aluminum, when he chanced upon a
crystalline substance. Curious, he exposed it to water,
and found that it gave off a highly-inflammable gas:
acetylene. The substance was carbide. Willson failed
in his bid to make this gas the fuel to light the city
streets of Canada, but he did succeed in designing
several acetylene marine signals, and as the pioneer of
the giant carbide industries of Canada and the United
States, he became known as "Carbide" Willson.*

CHARLES GOODEVE

War is the Great Destroyer, yet ironically no other time is as taxing of man's creative ingenuity and inventiveness. To Charles Goodeve, a young Manitoban in the Royal Navy, went one of the most critical challenges of World War II. His assignment: to find the means to stop the enemy's deadly magnetic mines from taking their devastating toll of British ships and sailors. He found not one but two solutions, the first by wiping the hulls of ships with a copper cable carrying an electric current, the second by planting "degaussing" cables inside ships' hulls. In 1940 Goodeve was made deputy director of the Department of Miscellaneous Weapon Development, and in charge of creating new secret weapons. Some of the devices he promoted were the Oerlikon anti-aircraft gun, the Hedgehog antisubmarine gun, as well as the floating Mulberry harbour. He was created O.B.E., 1941; and K.B., 1946.

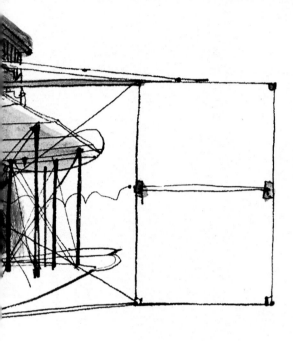

WALLACE RUPERT TURNBULL

Canada's first aeronautical theorist, Wallace Rupert Turnbull's chief claim to fame was his invention of the variable-pitch propeller, although he was recognized as one of the world's leading authorities in aerodynamics long before he began his research on this device in 1916. Working in his makeshift laboratory in Rothesay, N.B., as early as 1902 Turnbull was pioneering experiments in North America on wing angles and aerofoils, in Canada's first wind tunnel, and his treatise on dihedral angles of wings published in 1907 significantly affected the design of future aircraft. He won wide recognition for his research in hydroplanes and air-screws, and during World War I he co-operated with the British Government on many experiments, including the use of screens in anti-submarine warfare. No other Canadian did as much to enhance Canada's stature as a pioneer nation in aviation.

PHILIP McGINNIS

*"They're at the post . . . they're off!" And that's when
the squabbling began, at least in the years before
Philip McGinnis perfected his starting gate to put fair
play into the "sport of kings." Prior to his invention,
horses lined up at the post with no barrier in front of
them, and the race began with the throwing of a flag.
Nervous jockeys and horses sometimes jumped the flag,
and there were constant quarrels over unfair starts.
McGinnis, a race-track reporter from Huntingdon,
Quebec, solved the problem with a wire barrier which
flew up and allowed every horse an equal get-away.
Before they were replaced by electric gates, his starting
barriers were standard equipment at almost every race
track in North America.*

E. W. LEAVER

World War II had just ended when this Canadian envisaged an era that had not yet dawned — the age of automated production. In 1945, E. W. Leaver conceived of a "hand-arm machine," a device which could be used in industry to give machines the dexterity of the human arm, hand and wrist. It was only theory in 1946 when his ideas of "The Automatic Factory" appeared in print, but it stirred the imagination of industrialists and manufacturers the world over. Putting his theory into tangible form, in 1947 Leaver and a colleague, G. R. Mounce, built the world's first automatically controlled machine tool, in Toronto. It not only could equal a skilled workman using a lathe, but could record the operation in its "memory," and could repeat it automatically. He called his system Automatic Machine Control by Recorded Operation, or AMCRO.

6 / COMMUNICATIONS
The voice from afar

Whenever we pick up a phone, open a picture magazine, switch on the radio or send a telegram, we are in debt to a Canadian inventor. All these modern means of communication, each of which changed our world, would not have been possible without the inventive genius of men like Bell, Desbarats, Gisborne, Creed, Stevenson and Rogers.

Alexander Graham Bell is the giant: his telephone changed the world, revolutionizing both business and leisure. While the Scottish-born Bell is heartily acclaimed as an American hero, there is no doubt that he conceived the idea of the telephone while residing at Brantford, Ontario, and designed the first major part of his basic equipment there. The Bell house, Tutelo Heights, on a bend of the Grand River, is an historic site and the town boasts an imposing memorial unveiled in 1917 in the presence of the inventor himself. In 1954 the Federal Government financed the construction of the Bell Museum of Baddeck, Nova Scotia, where the great man built a permanent home in 1892. The museum houses Bell's notebooks and extensive photographic collection illustrating his many inventions, and working models of his devices. These include among many others – the first iron lung, metal-detection equipment, and a machine for making salt water drinkable.

Of the other "greats", George Desbarats' system for half-tone reproduction of photographs made the illustrated magazine possible; Gisborne, Creed and Stevenson between them supplied the basic elements of the modern newspaper; Rogers pioneered our home entertainment.

The steam foghorn

"The man who invented that fog whistle should get to heaven if anyone does," said a grizzled sea captain to his passengers, when, after a stormy passage across the Bay of Fundy the distinctive notes of Robert Foulis' invention were heard, and the ship was guided through the fog to shelter in the harbour of Saint John.

No one knows when the idea of marking treacherous reefs and rocky headlands by means of sound-making devices began, but it must have been early in the history of sea navigation. By the middle of the 19th century, great bells rocked by the motion of the sea were widely used. Off New Brunswick, there was a bell run by clockwork which would sound even when the sea was calm. Bells could not be heard very far, however, and even powerful lights were little use in fog.

Robert Foulis, a handsome New Brunswicker, was a successful portrait painter before turning his mind to mechanical things. His masterpiece, the first steam fog-horn in the world, was installed in 1859. It provided mariners with the best method of pinpointing dangers in fog for one hundred years, until loran and radar took over in the middle of the 20th century. Foulis also hit upon the idea of automatically coding the blasts of sound through the steam whistle. This meant that a mariner hearing the sound not only knew he was near land, but could also tell from the pattern of short and long blasts exactly what piece of land was in the offing. This provided the information he

Now, bits of gossip could be shared faster.

needed to get back on a safe course.

Beyond the heartfelt gratitude of all seamen, Foulis got no reward for his invention. A contemporary newspaper account says that a "trusting disposition was his undoing." Foulis had many talents and many interests and such people tend to flit from one absorbing idea to another, leaving a trail of unfinished business. His obituary lists his accomplishments as "surgeon, artist, engineer, mechanical and civil, engraver, inventor, foundryman, lecturer, scientist." As a factory owner in Saint John, he was the first to import pig iron into New Brunswick, and the first to manufacture cut nails.

The greatest idea of modern times

Alexander Graham Bell's success in inventing the telephone was, in some measure, due to the fact that he didn't know enough electrical theory to realize it simply wouldn't work. Most great inventions are the work of many men; the telephone is unique in that it had relatively few forebears, and seemed to spring, almost fully developed, out of one man's mind.

In the fall of 1871, Bell was appointed Professor of Vocal Physiology at Boston University. He spent his days teaching the deaf and his nights working on an improvement of the telegraph. Every summer he was back at Brantford conferring with his father, Alexander Melville Bell, and continuing his experiments there. By March 1875, Bell had taken out patents on the harmonic telegraph and had demonstrated it successfully to officials of Western Union.

The plush-paneled splendour of an early telephone booth: a far cry from the utilitarian glass cages of today, but a fitting surrounding for what was then a luxury, one that few Canadians could afford in their homes. In recent times, Canadians won the statistical distinction of talking more on their telephones than any other people in the world.

85

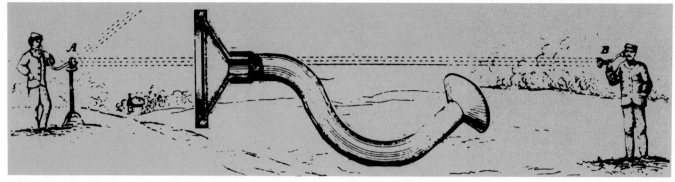

Bell's photophone: sound waves from a transmitter vibrate a ray of light, and the receiver converts changes in light intensity back to sound.

The three strange objects above are the ancestors of every telephone in the world. The one at the top is Bell's famed "gallows frame," which started it all in 1875. The models are in the Bell Museum at Baddeck.

Two months later, Bell wrote to his parents that "the transmission of the human voice is much more nearly at hand than I had supposed." Those summers at Brantford, when he could talk over his dreams and aspirations with his knowledgeable father, had done the trick. That fall, toiling full time with his thin-faced assistant, Thomas Watson, the square-bearded Bell was able to verify by experiment his idea of the telephone conceived at Brantford the following summer.

The key difference between Bell's telephone and all previous approaches to sending sound over wire was that his telephone required a continuous current. The words were sent by means of variations in the current, rather than by stopping the current and having it start up again, in a series of pulses. This "undulatory" current, as Bell called it, was seen at once to vary in intensity as air varied in density during the production of the sound. This was all Bell needed to confirm his theory. Watson was set to work immediately to make the first electrical speaking telephone. This was built and patented in 1876.

Back in Brantford again for the summer, Bell was eager to demonstrate his new telephone. He had two reasons for haste. First, he needed money badly and no doubt hoped that demonstrations of the instrument in actual use would loosen the notoriously tight purse strings of his conservative Ontario friends and potential investors. Second, and probably more important (because Bell never showed much interest in the financial side of his inventions), he wanted long-distance tests to improve his techniques.

Operating over a telegraph line designed for heavy currents, his instrument was plagued by high noise levels. The world's first long-distance call was made between Mount Pleasant and Brantford on August 3, 1876. At first the voices did not come through clearly at all, but when Bell ordered the instruments changed over to high-resistance coils the noise level dropped as if by magic. On August 10, an even longer distance was covered between Brantford and Paris, using power derived from a battery in Toronto, 68 miles away. The instrument was essentially the same as the telephone receiver in use today.

Bell not only originated and patented everything but, from the beginning, had a broad general concept of the form and social importance of the entire telephone system. Right from the start, in his mind's eye, he saw central exchanges, long-distance calls, automatic switching, and all the basic telephone technology which we accept today without a second's thought.

This curious device, made to Bell's instructions by Thomas Cowherd of Brantford, was produced at a reception at Tutelo Heights on August 4, 1876. A wire had been strung along fenceposts to the telegraph line at the main road; over it, the fascinated guests could hear songs and music and, of course, a speech.

At left, *the rescue of the incompleted trans-Atlantic cable. Snapped during a storm, it had to be recovered from the sea's bottom, then attached to a buoy until the cable could be spliced.*

Fred Gisborne's undersea cable

The honour of laying the first successful submarine cable in North America belongs to a Canadian, Frederick N. Gisborne. Although he had the rugged look of an outdoorsman, which he was, he was also chief executive of the Nova Scotia Telegraph Company.

In 1849 Gisborne suggested to the Newfoundland Government that the island should be connected to the mainland by an undersea cable. Gisborne had already won local renown building telegraph lines in Nova Scotia and New Brunswick. His plan was to run an overland line from St. John's to Cape Ray, over 400 miles of very difficult terrain, and then to use submarine cable between Cape Ray and Cape Breton. The Newfoundland Legislature granted 500 pounds ster-

ling for an initial survey of the land route. The survey party suffered appalling hardship, during which one member of the party died, and the remainder nearly perished of starvation.

Gisborne raised more money in New York, then sailed immediately for England to buy submarine cable. At this stage, he decided to first try a cable over the shorter distance between Prince Edward Island and New Brunswick. This line was successfully laid in the summer of 1852. This was the first submarine cable in North America and a major triumph for a country where both technical and financial skill was hard to find. Eventually, Gisborne played an important part in laying the trans-Atlantic cable, and went on to produce many inventions in the electrical and signalling fields. He died in 1892.

Pictures for the Press

The picture magazine, which dominates printed communications today, got its start when George Desbarats, of Ottawa, and his engraver, William Leggo, worked out the first practical system of making half-tones by rephotographing pictures through a fine screen. Although several systems capable of providing high-quality photographs for illustrating magazines existed by 1869, there was no way to reproduce photographs in quantity.

Desbarats, who had been Queen's Printer, put out the *Canadian Illustrated News*, the first publication in the world to use half-tone reproductions of photographs. It was an instant success because it gave readers actual photographs instead of "artist's conceptions" of major events. Desbarats' invention was in practical use a full decade before Ives and Levy in the u.s., or Jaffe or Meisenbach in Europe, came out with their half-tone processes. Today we use a mixture of all three.

In 1873, Desbarats and Leggo went to New York where they founded the *Daily Graphic*. This was the first daily newspaper in the United States to use half-tone illustrations.

Words from holes in a tape

Fred Creed was born at Mill Village, a hamlet between Halifax and Yarmouth, in 1871. He had only elementary education when he got his first job as a message boy in the telegraph office. He quickly learned the Morse code and, at 18, got a job as a Morse operator in Peru.

In the rugged isolation of the east coast of Newfoundland, at Heart's Content off Trinity Bay, the first trans-Atlantic cable station was built. Here on July 27, 1866 the submarine cable was landed by the ship Great Eastern, *linking the New World to the Old.*

This was the cover of Volume 1, Number 1, of the Canadian Illustrated News, *October 30, 1869 — the first publication to use half-tone photo reproduction. The photograph of Queen Victoria's son was taken by Canadian pioneer photographer, William Notman.*

By this time, telegraphy had already been greatly improved over the original Morse system. Transmission and reception of signals had been made automatic by means of punched tapes. Yet the tape had to be punched by hand at a rate of not over fourteen words a minute before it could be put into the Wheatstone transmitter, which put the signal on the line in accordance with the pattern of punched holes. Fred Creed found punching tape extremely tedious. He began to cast about for some way to make the job easier.

By a stroke of luck he had taken an old typewriter to Peru. Now he tried to rebuild it in such a way as to have the punched strip produced by the typewriter keys. A typical Nova Scotian, he was handy with a penknife and mechanically ingenious, and so, for his first machine, he actually whittled all the necessary parts from hardwood. The machine worked quite well for the input side, and can be considered the first keyboard perforator. The other half of the process, that of converting electric signals at the other end of the line into a punched strip, and then in turn into printed characters, was much more difficult.

In a sense, Morse's original receiver for the magnetic telegraph had been a printing instrument, for the stylus produced dots and dashes on a moving strip of paper. But these could be read only by an experienced operator and even then, rather slowly. All early attempts to reduce the electrical signal to Roman type were complicated, finicky and cumbersome. Creed's method had the basic virtue of simplicity.

The working model he brought

The camera ousts the artist

This photograph of Indians at an 1869 lacrosse tournament was the first inside picture in the Canadian Illustrated News *reproduced using George Desbarats' half-tone technique. It marked the beginning of the day when cameramen would replace illustrators in depicting major events.*

The old and the new: pen and ink drawing was combined with Canadian-invented half-tone photo reproduction on the front page of New York's Daily Graphic *on March 4, 1880.*

back to Halifax in 1895 finally got him some financial support in Glasgow the following year. By 1898, after many frustrations – and two years of dire poverty – he succeeded in selling his first keyboard perforator to the British Post Office. This is the one now exhibited in the Kensington Museum in London. At about the same time he sold his system to the Great Northern Telegraph Company.

Frederick Creed's receiving perforators and keyboard perforators were both powered by compressed air and made a deafening racket but, until his dying day, Creed mistrusted electricity and electronics. He felt that mechanical action was best because it was always positive and dependable.

The advent of wirephoto

Anyone who comes up with a badly needed invention – one that saves millions of dollars a year – gets rich, if he protects his idea at law. William Stephenson was a millionaire before he was 30, whereupon he retired from the inventing business and went into another line of work. He is famous today as the hero of cloak-and-dagger international spying episodes in World War II. The book about him, *The Quiet Canadian*, deals chiefly with his work as head of espionage and counter-espionage in Washington and London.

Born in Winnipeg, Stephenson graduated from the University of Manitoba, where he showed an early interest in radio. By 1921 he had worked out a basic concept for sending pictures over a wire and had tried, unsuccessfully, to interest Can-

William Stephenson, shown here at his wireless photography transmitter, made it possible for newspapers to receive photographs of distant events while the news was still breaking.

adian newspapers and electrical companies in his invention. In England, he had better success. By April 1923, he had all his models made and demonstrated, and had applied for his basic British patent No. 218766.

Stephenson's invention consisted of a brilliant application of the disc described by the German physicist Nipkow back in 1883. But Stephenson, instead of using one rotating disc, used two. The overlapping rotating discs, each provided with radial slits, were so arranged that a strong light shining through them formed a spot at the junction of the slits. As the discs rotated this spot moved across the picture from left to right then back across from right to left a little lower down. The intensity of the flying spot of light varies, depending on what part of the picture it hits. This varying intensity is translated into electrical impulses which can be sent any distance either over wires or by radio. At the receiving end, say at a newspaper office, the converse of the transmitting station is set up. Here the electrical impulses are changed into corresponding intensities of light on the flying spot, and a picture is formed on the screen at the same moment that the original picture is being scanned at the transmitting station.

The device of Stephenson, and his English partner George Walton, was an instant commercial success. It was picked up by the British newspapers because it filled a long-felt need of the communications industry for a system that would allow pictures transmitted anywhere in the world to be reproduced instantly in the London newspapers. The Stephenson system of radio facsimile, in its essentials, is still in use by newspapers everywhere.

Music in the groove

The phonograph, which has provided jobs for thousands and pleasure for millions, is of mixed parentage but, in practical terms, Canada figures largely in the story. The idea was sketched in principle by Edison in 1877, but the quality of his sound was terrible and nothing much developed for twenty years. It remained for Bell and Berliner to come up with commercially feasible methods of sound recording – essentially the ones we use today.

In recognition of his invention of the telephone, the French Government awarded the Volta Prize to Bell. With the money, he set up the Volta Laboratories in Washington, D.C., where he worked with two associates, his cousin Chichester Bell and Sumner Tainter. When the Volta associates became interested in recording sound, they produced the same wax cylinder that is used to this day. It is on this that the modern record industry is founded. The Columbia Phonograph Company was formed to exploit the commercial possibilities of Bell's "graphophone."

The impressively high quality of sound from the machine arose partly from the good recording qualities of wax – as opposed to Edison's tinfoil – partly from a more refined stylus and diaphragm design made possible by Bell's knowledge of the art, but chiefly because, instead of having the stylus make indentations like dots and dashes as in the Edison machine, the Bell stylus was able to cut a smooth wavy groove in the cylinder as it rotated.

Well before the turn of the century, Montreal workers were already recording music on flat discs of wax – the next major step. This marked the great contribution of Emile Berliner who, in 1889, in partnership with E. R. Johnson, of Camden, New Jersey, set up manufacture as the Berliner Company in Montreal.

The Volta associates had earlier experimented with the flat disc, using the Edison system of "hill and dale," or vertical, recording. This meant that the needle, in recording variations of sound, moved vertically. Berliner's contribution was "lateral recording" where the needle cut a groove of constant depth but moved fractionally from side to side to reproduce the sound waves. With this method, records could be inexpensively mass-produced, and it became the basic recording system until magnetic tapes took over in the 1950s.

Ted Rogers' radio tube

Late in the evening of August 4, 1914, a boy sat hunched over the home-built collection of wires and tubes he called a "wireless." Suddenly, amid the howls and squeaks of the short-wave broadcast from London, came the announcement that England had declared war on Germany. Thus Ted Rogers, at 14, achieved a certain local fame by announcing the beginning of World War I, well ahead of the local newspapers.

It is difficult now, when not only radio but colour television is commonplace, for us to imagine what

Ted Rogers in his Toronto workshop, 1922: he developed the AC tube that allowed radios to be operated with ordinary house electric current.

radio was like in those days. Rogers grew up in the exciting days when radio communication was almost a form of magic, yet anyone with a bit of ingenuity could rig up a crystal set that would pluck sounds from the empty air.

A precocious and enthusiastic experimenter, Rogers was not a great success at school. He graduated from Pickering College but, after a short time in engineering at the University of Toronto, he decided he could do better in the outside world. Luckily, he was a rich man's son so he was able to set up a laboratory and get to work on the projects he loved.

Ted's family, prominent in the business and social worlds of Toronto, wanted him to become a business executive. Instead, he sat in the family garage, endlessly working the transmitting key of his home-built radio station (3BP), broadcasting on a frequency of 300 meters with a half-kilowatt spark transmitter. His signals were heard as far away as the Pacific Coast. In 1921 he became the first Canadian amateur to successfully transmit a radio signal across the Atlantic.

One of the items that marred the radio listener's pleasure in the early days was the fact that batteries ran down. As this happened, the sound became progressively fainter. Batteries were expensive, bulky, and unreliable. About 1924, Ted Rogers decided that batteries must go. Radios must be operated on ordinary house current. Engineers ridiculed his scheme, pointing out, correctly, that if you used alternating current to heat the cathode inside the tube, the AC hum, instead of being merely annoying, would be deafening.

Rogers returned to his garage on Toronto's Chestnut Street and began a day-and-night search for a radio tube that could be run on alternating current. His first idea was fairly simple. He decided to bring the cathode leads out one end of the tube and the plate and grid leads out the other. This, at least, separated the two kinds of electricity as far as was possible in the physical dimensions of the tube. Next he had to find an insulator that would stand the heat generated by the cathode. Toward the end of 1924, he had worked out solutions to these and a host of other problems, including the means to avoid AC hum. In April 1925 he filed his patent application, which was granted as No. 269205 in March 1927.

The invention of the AC tube and the consequent "batteryless" radio gave young Ted Rogers a place in the history of communications technology, if not at the very top with Marconi, Bell and Baird, at least in the second rank with Edison and Popoff and his fellow Canadian Reginald Fessenden.

The invention turned out to be the key to making home radio reception popular. With a business acumen not usually found in young inventors, Rogers set up a new company to manufacture his tube and, in August 1925, the first commercial AC tube was turned out by the new Rogers Majestic Corporation, in Toronto.

7 / AUTOMATION
"Look, no hands!"

I simply don't know why Canadians were pioneers in automation – which we can call the production of goods and services without human aid. J. G. Wright, then a lowly lieutenant in the R.C.A.F., invented the first air navigation computer; E. W. Leaver, just after World War II, built the first automatically controlled machine tool; Larry Wilson made the special tabulator used for the world's first machine-made national census; Maurice Levy demonstrated the world's first automatic post office in Ottawa, to postal authorities from all over the world. Of these, by far the most important in terms of earning power was Eric Leaver's AMCRO (Automatic Machine Control by Recorded Operation).

One bright spring day in 1945 two young Canadians who had worked together during the war at the Government radar plant in Toronto were arguing about how war-developed devices were going to affect industry. Leaver, a stocky boyish tow-head who already had a string of patented inventions going back to the early Thirties, suddenly said: "I'll give you a specific example of how Selsyns* and other wartime stuff could be whipped together to make an entirely new type of machine tool." He then went on to describe, in considerable detail, what he called a "hand-arm machine."

The human hand is a masterpiece of mechanical articulation, controlled automatically by a beautiful set of short and long-loop feedback systems. Leaver argued that it was now possible to reproduce the mechanical articulations and even to make them so the machine equivalent of the human wrist could not only rotate through 180 degrees, but could rotate continuously in either direction. Moreover, the machine could be made much stronger than the human arm, wrist and fingers. Hence a hand-arm machine could be built that would be capable of lifting and manipulating a two-ton steel billet under the blows of the forging hammer.

His listener argued that such machines would be expensive while labour was cheap. Moreover, everybody knew the world was entering a post-war depression and that labour would become even more available

*Electric devices for remote control of machines or instruments.

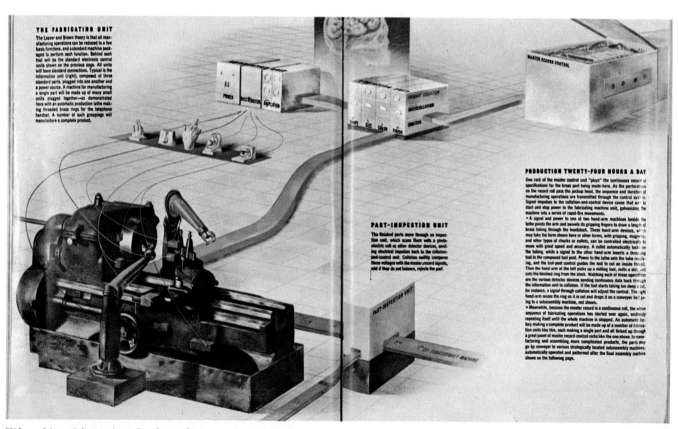

When this article (written by the author of this book) appeared in Fortune *in 1946, outlining Eric W. Leaver's concept of "The Automatic Factory," some manufacturers and businessmen dismissed Leaver's idea as something akin to science-fiction. Others, however, such as General Electric, saw tremendous commercial possibilities in the hand-arm machine, and they bought the rights to the basic idea. Leaver's AMCRO system became the starting point for the development of today's multi-billion dollar automatically-controlled machine tool industry. Leaver's system proved invaluable for machining the carving of wings for jet aircraft and for the manufacture of intricately-shaped parts previously produced by human operators.*

and cheaper. This was in 1945 – before the scientific journals had begun to publish reports on how the atomic bomb was built. Had Leaver known of some American, British and Canadian secret documents in this field, he would have been assured that the remote-control manipulator was very much a reality, and had been one of the means by which dangerous radioactive substances had been handled during the development of the atomic bomb.

Birth of the hand-arm

During the rest of 1945 and early 1946, Leaver thought more and more about the basic problems of working metals by the use of automatic machine tools. Then he worked out not only the basic design of a hand-arm machine that could function as either a remotely controlled or a programmed manipulator, but in addition carried his thinking much farther into the general field of making products without using the labour of men. After a characteristically thorough and critical study of all the ways of controlling machine tools automatically, he settled on the system which he called AMCRO. By mid-1946 these ideas were well enough developed to enable me to write a long article for *Fortune* called "The Automatic Factory." This contained illustrations and artist's concepts of both the hand-arm machine and automatically-controlled machine tools in operation in a factory. When my report appeared in the magazine, Leaver's ideas achieved immediate circulation all over the world.

In the meantime, at his company's small Toronto plant, Leaver, with the help of G. R. Mounce, a taciturn Nova Scotian who had been trained at Massachusetts Institute of Technology, built the first production tool capable of memorizing a skilled workman's operations and then playing them back to make a product. This basic invention, one of the first contributions to what is today the great field of automation, was operating in their Toronto plant by 1947 and people came from all over the world to see it.

The machine, attached to an ordinary nine-inch lathe, watches a skilled workman while he makes a simple part. While he is working, information relating to tool position, speed and the like is recorded. At the end of the series of operations the machine is loaded with fresh stock, the record switched to "playback" and a new part, which is a faithful reproduction of the sample, is turned out without any human intervention. The record can be played over and over again so that parts will be made as long as the machine contains raw stock. Canadian, U.S. and foreign patents were granted Leaver and Mounce in 1949.

The automatic control of machine tools can be achieved by various means. In the relatively simple "contour lathe" system, the cutting tool, while making a new part from bar stock, is made to follow the contours of a model or pattern (in simplest terms, this is how most home-owners get their keys duplicated in hardware stores). But the methods in use in today's automated factories are much more sophisticated. The information on which a machine tool depends for its control can, broadly speaking, be provided in two different forms. The first is analogue, which is information in a continuous form like the numbers on a slide rule. The other type is called digital. This is information in the form of discrete bits, like a list of figures in a table. Before deciding on the analogue system of information handling that is characteristic of AMCRO, Leaver tried other analogue systems as well as the major digital methods, and rejected them for various reasons. For example, the punched tape form of digital information which William M. Pease of M.I.T. developed later in the 1950s was rejected early by Leaver because of its expense and complexity. Five years after Leaver, the Pease system was splashed all over the newspapers as the latest product of American ingenuity.

A machine that drives a nail

In terms of dollar potential, the loss of AMCRO is probably the largest "missed boat" in the entire history of Canadian technology. Today, the automatic control of machine tools is a $1.2 billion business, and it is becoming more valuable every year. Leaver and Mounce were clearly the first into the field with a head start of about six years. But their little company, founded with $10,000 capital in 1945, was in no position to build a patent fence around the basic idea. Hence they were able to patent only one way of doing the job, and this left the field clear for the patenting by others of a whole range of alternative methods.

The hand-arm machine itself, to-

Conceived in Canada, manufactured in the States, this statistics machine unplugged the bottleneck that delayed census results. It automatically transferred information on to special cards.

day called an industrial manipulator, is now big business. In the late Forties, Leaver and Mounce tried to get government or private support for the further development of their patent in Canada but were unable to arouse any interest. Characteristically, when support finally came, it was from an American company.

Most major machine-tool builders in the United States now have hand-arm machines of one kind or another. One type of programmed manipulator can do a repetitive job over and over again. It can be set either to pick up a dozen ping-pong balls and pack them in a box, or to screw nuts on the end of short threaded pipes, or do any of a thousand other operations.

General Mills makes an underwater manipulator for the u.s. Navy which bears an uncanny resemblance to Leaver's original hand-arm machine. In the missile laboratories and the atomic energy laboratories there are many types of hand-operated, remote-control manipulators. One is dextrous enough to drive a nail into a piece of wood by remote control; another can be programmed to pick up a bowling ball, place it on the return rack and then go back to pick up another.

More and more machines of this type are being adapted to assembly-line jobs such as loading and unloading parts into machines, shifting parts into and out of stamping or welding jigs, or spray painting irregularly shaped products. Hand-arm machines alone today are a multi-million-dollar business, and Canadian companies are beginning to buy them from u.s., German, and English suppliers.

Larry Wilson's census machine

Now in universal use by governments of the Western world, the i.b.m. 101 statistical machine is a happy example of close co-operation between Canadian and u.s. scientists in both government and business. The machine was conceived in Canada and brought to conclusion, under strong Canadian pressure, by i.b.m. in the United States. After the 1941 Canadian census (which used punched cards) it took eleven years to get all the results published. The then Prime Minister, W. L. Mackenzie King, who had been trained as an economist, wanted the process speeded up and he kept constant pressure on the Dominion Bureau of Statistics to find some way of getting census figures out quickly. In the Ottawa of the 1940s, pressure from Mackenzie King was something to be reckoned with.

But by this time a Canadian, Marshall, had caught Larry Wilson's enthusiasm. Punched cards had been used as the information source on machines in the 17th and 18th century, and Wilson argued cogently that they were obsolete for use in the 20th because they did not work fast enough. Marshall was convinced that Wilson's ideas would provide the required speed. In due course i.b.m. came around and agreed to do the development job, provided that Wilson would come to work for them at Endicott, New York. Wilson has since been promoted with i.b.m. and is now an i.b.m. Fellow at the Development Laboratories in San Jose, California.

The problem of the transfer of information to the cards from the census takers' memoranda was a difficult one. The card that had been in use previously for the Canadian census was not suited to Wilson's approach. Thinking about this hurdle one day in the d.b.s. building on the Rideau River, Wilson suddenly jumped up, saying, "I've got it." He took off immediately for Endicott to try the idea on the prototype machine, and the following afternoon called Ottawa saying that the system worked. Some weeks later the public demonstration of the 101 was given at Endicott.

Thus, the 1951 census in Canada marked the first breakthrough in any country away from handwritten documents completed by the enumerator to form the basis of punched cards, and toward the "mark sensing" system. Most of the u.s. Census executives, when this idea was first broached, did not think the system would work. The idea and invention came from Canada; the hardware from the United States. As a result of this co-operation, a new tool was put at the disposal of the world's demographers.

In about 1947, J. T. Marshall of the d.b.s. called Dr. Halbert L. Dunn of the u.s. Bureau of the Census about the problem. Dunn had working for him at this time a young statistician named Larry Wilson who had some specific ideas about what a census-oriented machine should be like. Thus reinforced, the Census men took Wilson with them for a frontal assault, first on Remington Rand, and when that failed, on i.b.m., in the person of Thomas J. Watson, Sr., but again the answer was "no." The president didn't want to have anything to do with electronics: he was a metal-finger-making-contact-with-a-brass-plate man from away back.

No matter how fast the plane, train or ship that carried the mail, there were delays at both sending and receiving ends, as letters piled up waiting to be sorted by hand according to destination. To quicken the postal pace, an automatic mail sorter was needed, and in the 1950s Canada was leading the world in the development of an automatic post office, thanks to Dr. Maurice Levy, shown here with his brainchild. From the U.S., England and Germany, postal delegates came to study this machine-age marvel. Most who saw it in operation were impressed ... but not the Canadian Government. It closed down the laboratory.

W. J. Turnbull: he saw the need for a coding system to speed up mail sorting.

The net result of this project was that, instead of taking eleven years to get full use out of the census as it did in 1941, it took barely three years to get the 1951 census results published. This happened in spite of a tremendous increase in the amount of material handled.

It is hard to understand the rate at which information grows in a technologically oriented society. The 1951 census had 27 million "cells of information." The basic number for the 1961 census was 68 milion, and by the Centennial it was estimated that this would have increased to 198 million. Had the change not been made from the old mechanical method to the new electronic means of information handling, census results would become available so slowly as to be virtually useless.

The automatic post office

Hundreds of millions of dollars a year are now being spent by the advanced nations of the world for the automatic handling of incoming and outgoing mail. The automatic post office is now an absolute necessity for any nation enjoying a high rate of growth. In the mid 1950s, Canada was fast off the mark and within a few years enjoyed a commanding lead in the race for the automatic electronic post office. The Postmaster-General himself declared in 1957 that "Canada was leading the world" in this field. A constant stream of specialists from the U.S. and Europe were visiting the $2 million electronic post office installation in Ottawa.

Canada's short-lived, but spectacular, lead in the electronic post office came about as the result of the meeting of a New Canadian who wouldn't take "no" for an answer, and an unusually intelligent Deputy Postmaster-General. Dr. Maurice Levy, a small dark man with piercing eyes, was born and trained in France. He worked briefly in Ottawa for the Defence Research Board before being taken on as a consultant to the Canadian Post Office. The Deputy Postmaster-General of the time, W. J. Turnbull, had, late in 1951, set up a study to see whether coding methods could be applied to mail sorting. Levy's flint and Turnbull's steel struck fire, and Levy was appointed as a consultant to the department, charged with developing electronic sorting methods.

To understand the magnitude of the problem, you have to know something about how mail comes into a city post office and is sorted by destination. The city of Toronto, for example, is divided into some ten thousand sections or "walks." The sorter must memorize the section to which a particular address belongs before he can allocate the letter to the proper carrier. To make these "sorts" quickly, the man must not only have a good memory for the original breakdown of districts or walks, but also have total recall for modifications that come in constantly as new buildings are built and routes changed. In addition, the sorter must not lose efficiency as he gets tired. Since the number of separate sortings is at least four for city-to-city mail, the opportunities for error are numerous indeed.

Levy saw at once that the perfect solution is to devise a machine that can look at the address written on the envelope, read it, choose from the ten thousand possible sections the one that is right, and then shoot the letter into the proper bin. In order to handle the volume of mail coming into a big city, the machine should be able to do this at the rate of 60 letters a second, or more than 200,000 an hour. Machines operating at this speed work so fast that the mechanical motions are invisible to the naked eye. If anything goes wrong (as it often does) the room is under a snowstorm of letters before anyone can hit the panic button to stop the machine.

Levy's first idea was to work out some method of reading hand-written addresses on envelopes, but he soon gave this up as being too difficult for machines in their present state of evolution. Then he worked out the simpler process of coding the envelopes to solve his problem. The machine he developed carried the letters, one at a time, before a human operator who read the address and then used a keyboard to punch the code representing that address. This code was printed on the back of the letter. Then the automatic route computer, following the instructions given in the code, dropped each letter into the proper outgoing bag.

As work progressed and articles about the automatic post office began appearing in technical journals, foreign post office officials began arriving in Ottawa. The U.S. sent a group of Congressmen to check up on the Canadian invention before Congress voted $5 million to a research laboratory in Washington for similar study. England and Germany sent postal delegations to see the machine in opera-

tion. Levy claimed that by early 1959 the equipment was working at 98 per cent efficiency, and sorting mail by electronics was a reality in Canada.

The politicians at Ottawa thought differently, however, and they closed the door on the post office laboratory in Ottawa – on what most people would call a highly successful operation. By so doing, the door was closed on an opportunity to get in on the ground floor of an export trade now worth $300 million a year.

Flying planes automatically

Canada's first contribution to aircraft navigation was probably the R Theta computer, invented by Wing Commander J. G. Wright, of Liverpool, Nova Scotia. This was the first practical navigating instrument that was completely automatic. It allows the pilot of the fighter aircraft to give full attention to firing his guns instead of worrying about where he is in the air. In 1954 Wright was awarded the McKee Trophy for this important contribution to aeronautics.

Many world airlines are now using a radar system made in Canada which shows an aircraft's position continuously relative to its destination. The Canadian Marconi Company was the first to produce "Doppler" radar commercially. K. C. M. Clegg, chief engineer of the commercial products division of this company, should get the credit for producing Doppler radar successfully in Canada in the face of tough international competition. In 1964, he was given the McCurdy Award by the Canadian Aeronautics and Space Institute.

The flight simulators for training

The flight simulator provides rookie pilots with all the sensations of flying, without exposing them to dangers in the air during their first lessons. Years ahead in development, Canadian jet-flight simulators are widely acclaimed.

The Codatron was invented by Torontonian G. R. Mounce, to sort telephone and mail orders for a drug company. It replaced 30 card-pickers on roller skates.

pilots of jet aircraft, made by Canadian Aviation Electronics, of Montreal, are one of Canada's best-known inventions abroad. In them, the green pilot "flies" the plane under every kind of imaginable circumstance without ever leaving the ground. Under the leadership of Ken Patrick, the company got a big head start on corresponding groups in the United States and the United Kingdom. The Canadian flight simulators – especially those for jet transports – were a full generation ahead of those in other parts of the world. The company still enjoys a considerable lead in this and related fields.

While not connected with aeronautical engineering, Air Canada's "ReserVec" system plays an important role in air transport operations. This is a computer to handle reservations, conceived and designed by Canadians. The electronic reservation system has been in use since 1961, and is still a leader.

Eliminating human error

The only important business machine invented by a Canadian is the Codatron input device invented by G. R. Mounce in Toronto. All our data-processing systems depend for their effectiveness on the speed and accuracy with which the basic information can be inserted. If the basic information is wrong, nothing works. If the information input to the machine is too slow, data processing is too expensive.

Input data for modern computers can take the form of punched cards, punched paper tape, magnetic tape, or a magnetic drum. A fertile source

of error and consequent frustration in the use of computers is the point where a human operator, working from a handwritten form, such as an order, prepares an input device such as a punched card. Codatron eliminates, at one blow, the main problems met when the operator tries to code input information on punched cards. What the machine does is make precoded data available on a single punched card at the push of a single button. This eliminates the steps of looking up a code by hand, punching the card, and then verifying the information on it. By eliminating people from this part of the operation, speed is doubled and human error eliminated.

The electron microscope

Perhaps the outstanding example of new technology produced by university research teams is the development of the electron microscope in North America by members of the physics department of the University of Toronto. The team, headed by Professor E. F. Burton, already famed for his work on liquid helium, as well as in superconductivity, consisted of C. E. Howe, Ely Berton and James Hillier.

The basic concept of the electron microscope came from Germany in the late 1920s, but Burton's team in Toronto must get the credit for being the first group to make it a practical commercial device. Now, it has become an indispensable tool in research laboratories all over the world, in medicine and in day-to-day inspection in highly developed industries, such as drug manufacturing.

James Hellier (above) *was one of the team of four University of Toronto physicists who gave the world the first commercially practical electron microscope.*

The reaper. an answer to a labour shortage.

8 / FEEDING THE WORLD
Five brilliant ideas

If Canada has some of the world's best-fed people, it is partly because of the largely unrewarded labours of a failed musician, three medical doctors, a government scientist, and a minister of the gospel. Every time we eat a slice of bread we enjoy the benefit of the life work of Charles Saunders, whose early-ripening and disease-resistant wheats made Canada the granary of the world. All over North America, babies get off to a good start with Pablum, the invention of three Toronto doctors. Frozen foods, perhaps the greatest convenience product of the century, began in Halifax as a by-product of Archibald Huntsman's work in fisheries research. Thousands of jobs, and millions of dollars' worth of annual trade, can be traced directly to a handful of Canadians who were not satisfied with conventional methods of growing and marketing food.

The sea of wheat from the Prairies could not flow fast enough without our ultra-modern farm machinery. The ancestor of this industry was the Rev. Patrick Bell, from St. Andrews University, in Scotland. Some time between 1830 and 1832, when he was 27, he put together a reaper that contained just about all the elements used in the modern machine. To the cutter bar and rotating reel, which had already been invented in England, he added an endless conveyor belt made of canvas which carried the cut grain out of the machine and formed it into a sheaf.

Bell appeared in Upper Canada in 1833 to serve as tutor to the family of Adam Ferguson, at Fergus, in Western Ontario. He brought a model of his reaper with him. There was a shortage of labour of every kind in pioneer Canada and farm labour was particularly difficult because everybody's grain ripened at the same time.

The idea of mechanizing the harvest was eagerly welcomed and, when the Patent Office opened for business in Canada in June 1824, no fewer than seven of the first thirty patents issued were concerned with threshing machines. All of them were, however, of the stationary type – they were to be installed in the barn where the grain had to be brought for threshing.

A bushel in three minutes

Nobody knows whether or not the Rev. Bell tried to sell his invention in Upper Canada, but within a year or two after he arrived at least two threshing machines were being developed in the province. John Fisher, a blacksmith of Hamilton, had probably the first Canadian-made threshing machine. Between 1833 and 1837, financed from New York, he completed a device which was an improvement on an earlier thresher. This machine was later turned over to Sawyer Brothers, whose business was absorbed in the Sawyer & Massey Company. Some of its basic principles are still in use today.

In October 1835, the Montreal *Gazette* quoted the *Christian Guardian* as follows: "We understand that a Mr. F. Williams in the Township of Whitby has invented what he calls a harvesting machine which gathers, threshes and rough cleans wheat, barley, etc. at the rate of a bushel in three minutes. The machine may be worked by horse or steampower." Since neither the Fisher nor the Williams machine was patented, very little is known about them. They were probably manufactured, if at all, in small numbers for purely local use.

As early as 1830, Daniel Massey had come to Ontario with a "bull thresher," the heavy machine used in the barn. In 1847 he set up a small shop to manufacture farm implements at the village of Bond Head, on Lake Ontario. The next year he moved the enterprise to a larger site nearby, and called his company the Newcastle Foundry & Machine Manufactory, Canada West. Here he began to manufacture some American farm machinery under license. The most important among these was the famous mower invented by W. F. Ketchum, of Buffalo, New York. In 1852 Hart Massey, who had succeeded his father, built the first mowers in Canada under the Ketchum license.

Pull became push on Rev. Bell's remarkable reaper, designed in the 1830s.

Joseph Hall of Oshawa turned out this handsome mobile thresher.

The Ayr Clipper *was invented by John Watson before 1871.*

103

Delivery Day for the shiny new-fangled farm machinery was a carnival in Canada's pioneer communities, with bands, banquets and speeches, and new

...wners proudly paraded their machines down Main Street. This was Stettler, Alberta.

The self-raking mowing machine may have been a Canadian invention. There is one in the Department of Agriculture Museum in Ottawa that was built by the Massey firm in 1862.

By the end of the 1860s, Canada had a small but useful farm-implement industry. The Harris family of Beamsville, the Patterson family of Richmond Hill, and William Ferrity of Francestown, Canada West, all had prosperous small plants manufacturing farm equipment, mostly of their own invention. The Wisner family of Bedford, who specialized in the manufacture of fanning mills, was another important early producer.

When the railroads pushed west to link the new nation coast to coast, inventors began devising equipment for special local conditions. The Noble family of Alberta, for example, produced a line of weeders and land-clearing equipment suitable for the Prairies.

Canadian farm-equipment manufacture probably reached its highest development with Thomas Carroll's self-propelled combine harvester. The first model came out in 1937, and was used as far away as the Argentine. During World War II these self-propelled combines were used by the "Harvest Brigades" to overcome the shortage of farm labour. About 500 of the machines, built by Massey Harris, moved across the country for these wartime harvests – a veritable revolution in mechanized agriculture.

Lock Lever Sulkey Hay Rake: circa 1870.

In 1871, this mower was a proud product from Whitby, Ontario.

Guaranteed to gather crowds at farm fairs and festivals across the country were exhibitions showing how machines could cut down chores for the farmers. This early sketch shows excited spectators waving hats and hankies, cheering on an engine from Brantford, Ontario, as it performed its wonders.

Saunders developed the Marquis wheat that made Canada a great agricultural nation.

Charles Saunders' Marquis wheat

One of the great paradoxes of Canadian history is that Charles Saunders, a sick man who couldn't make a living as a musician in Toronto, added more wealth to his country than anyone before or since. In a recent year Canada exported over $600 millions' worth of wheat and flour. Without Saunders' brilliant research we could not, perhaps, grow enough wheat for our own needs, instead of being able to supply vast quantities to the undeveloped nations of the world.

Charles Saunders' real interest was music. Born in London, Ontario, in 1867, he had – under the urging of a strong-willed father – graduated in chemistry from the University of Toronto and then taken a Ph.D. at Johns Hopkins. He taught chemistry for a while but soon resigned to try his luck as a music teacher and a flutist in Toronto. He wasn't aggressive enough to go out and get pupils, and his career, and his health, failed. His father, William Saunders, stepped in again in a classic demonstration of nepotism.

Saunders, Sr., was an arrogant Victorian who knew exactly what he wanted. Starting out as a pharmacist in London, he had risen rapidly to head the Canadian Horticultural Society and, in 1884, had become the first director of the Dominion Experimental Farms. Before the Government's colonizing policy could be successfully carried out, Saunders had to develop a wheat suitable for the West. At that time, the small amount of wheat grown there was usually Red Fife, which ripened too late for prairie climates.

Saunders devoted several years to cross-breeding Red Fife with hundreds of other varieties from all parts of the world. He would cross Red Fife with, say, a Russian variety, and then select the most promising strain from their progeny, and plant again. But, as the years passed, his work as head of the expanding Dominion Experimental Farms allowed him less and less time to work on the development of cereals (in spite of the tremendous energy that permitted him to fire off 11,000 letters a year).

He persuaded the Government that the position of Dominion Cerealist should be created, and that his son be appointed to the job. Charles, with his excellent training in chemistry and instinct for research, was certainly a good appointment, but at first he refused to take the job. His father had him appointed to it anyway, and sent him a telegram telling him so.

In his drive to develop what became Marquis wheat, Charles Saunders inherited the results of the decade of experiments made by his father. Not long after he took over, Charles noticed a single head in an experimental plot of a variety of wheat called Markham. This was a cross between Red Fife and an Indian variety called Red Calcutta. The single head he noticed had 12 kernels of wheat. These were planted and, in time, produced a sufficient quantity of seed so that milling and baking tests could be carried out. These proved that the wheat was an excellent commercial type – but was it a genuine early-ripening variety?

In tests held in the harsh season of 1907-08, there were heavy losses by freezing of just about all varieties planted . . . except the new Marquis. The fame of Marquis spread rapidly all over the West, where it was found to mature about ten days earlier than the best varieties previously used. By 1920, ninety per cent of the wheat grown in the Prairies was Marquis.

Helping the harried housewife

Canadian pioneering in the mass production of food resulted in technical specialties which we export all over the world. Some of these exports of Canadian skills are hard to believe.

For example, cheddar cheese originated, of course, around the ancient town of the same name in the west of England yet it was a Canadian who taught the English how to mass produce it. Until nearly the end of the 19th century, cheddar continued to be made in small batches by cottage methods. In Canada, however, almost from the beginning, it had been made in cheese factories. By the 1880s the techniques had been standardized to such an extent in Canada that the product was essentially uniform, whether the cheese was made in a factory in Quebec, Ontario, or the Maritimes. A uniform product is a basic requirement of any modern mass-production process.

In 1889, the Ayrshire Dairy Association invited R. J. Drummond to visit England to teach the Canadian methods. Among other things, Drummond seems to have introduced the hot-iron test to determine whether a piece of curd was ripe enough to be pressed into a mold. This replaced an earlier method which was little more than an educated guess.

A. G. Huntsman: first frozen food

W. H. Cook: croquettes from powder

E. A. Asselbergs, through his "instant" potato flakes, may make kitchen potato peeling a lost art. Few housewives will mourn its passing.

As early as 1926, Dr. Archibald G. Huntsman, then of the Biological Board of Canada (which became the Fisheries Research Board), became interested in the marketing of fish. He became the first man in North America to freeze food commercially, and his researches resulted in the first successful marketing of frozen fish fillets. Later Colonel Clarence Birdseye, who got the idea from the reports of an Arctic expedition, made packaged frozen foods a major U.S. industry.

The instant potato

Dr. W. H. Cook, director of the division of bio-sciences at the National Research Council, developed a new method of making frozen dried food. This turns potatoes, fish, lamb or beef into a powder which can then be reconstituted with water to make croquettes. I can report that they taste about as good as croquettes can ever taste, namely not very. Nonetheless, this invention could have important consequences for Prince Edward Island; the province has a

Dr. Frederick Tisdall

Dr. Alan Brown

Dr. Theodore Drake and his famous collection. With Drs. Tisdall and Brown, he developed Pablum, one of the world's best known baby foods.

surplus of potatoes which are difficult to transport or store. By reducing them to an easily shipped powder, Cook's invention may well provide cheap food for the hungry millions of Asia. The method can also be applied to surplus catches of fish, and, in fact, to almost any vegetable or meat surplus.

"Instant" potato flakes represented another important development in the same field. This technique resulted from the work of Dr. E. A. Asselbergs, of the Federal Department of Agriculture.

First precooked cereal

Canada's best known contribution to the food business is, however, undoubtedly Pablum, the world's first precooked cereal. A time-saving boon to generations of young mothers, this universal baby food was developed by the Toronto doctors Frederick Tisdall, Theodore Drake, and Alan Brown in the 1930s. Dr. Drake donated the world-famous museum of pediatrics now housed in the Academy of Medicine.

9 / THE SPUR OF WAR
Defence and attack

When war breaks out, everybody – even the government – gets interested in inventions. If someone out there is trying to kill you it suddenly becomes urgent to know exactly where he is and what weapon he is likely to use, so you can have your defence, and, hopefully, better weapons, at the ready.

The effect of wartime inventions on peacetime industry is highly exaggerated, yet during both the 1914-18 and the 1939-45 wars, Canadians came up with ingenious schemes, some of which developed into large industries. The Canadian chemical industry, for instance, hit its stride only after the sudden push of World War I; the Commonwealth Air Training Plan and the Atlantic Ferry Command of World War II established Canada in international air transport.

The last war was only a few hours old when Charles Goodeve, a slight, intense young Canadian who had been on a scholarship at University College, London, found himself in the Royal Navy, charged with finding a quick answer to the German magnetic mine. It occurred to him he might combine schemes of two earlier investigators and he wrote a memorandum to this effect to Whitehall. Then, without waiting for a reply, he rushed out to Canoe Lake, near Portsmouth, and tested the idea, using a captured magnetic mine. It worked perfectly, and Goodeve returned to his office well pleased. He then had the exquisite satisfaction of finding this top secret memo on his desk:

You should discontinue any research on the lines you have indicated in your latest report. It is clear to me that the method you suggest would prove self-cancelling and cannot work.

Goodeve was born in Winnipeg and he graduated in science from the University of Manitoba; as an R.C.N. reservist, he had become the youngest commissioned officer in the service.

Following his triumph over the military bureaucracy in London, Goodeve was assigned permanently to Portsmouth to pursue his campaign against the magnetic mine which threatened Britain's shipping lifeline. Steel ships, when under construction, develop a magnetic charge like a compass needle, and it was this minute magnetic field which caused the mines to explode as the ship passed. If some way could be found to neutralize or reverse the ship's magnetic field, the mines would not explode. Earlier, the French Navy had

After the Germans had unleashed chlorine on Canadians in World War I, Dr. Cluny McPherson desperately fashioned the first rudimentary gas mask. Soon, a more sophisticated model was mass produced, and became standard equipment in Allied trenches.

made the suggestion that a ship's magnetism could be neutralized by passing it through a gigantic coil in which huge currents of electricity were flowing. This plan was very expensive and impractical because of its size, but Goodeve could not get the principle out of his mind.

By early 1940, Goodeve and his assistant, F. D. Richardson, had worked out the basic system for de-magnetizing ships that was used for the rest of the war. This was a brilliantly simple plan which could quickly be carried out. All that was required was to wipe the hulls with a copper cable carrying an electric current; a permanent "cure" called for the installation of a "degaussing" cable inside the ship's hull. Between May and June 1940 – that is, around the time of Dunkirk – two thousand ships were "degaussed" and a further thousand were wiped. As a result, of the 218 ships lost during the retreat from Dunkirk, only two were destroyed by magnetic mines.

The first degaussing range outside the British Isles was built in Bedford Basin, near Halifax. This permitted the measurement of a ship's magnetism to be made very accurately and then degaussing cables could be fitted inside the hull to counteract the ship's inherent magnetism. For the remainder of the war, thousands of ships from every nation were tested and degaussed there.

Gas mask and G-suit

The most important protective device of World War I was invented by a Canadian. When the German Army released poison gas at Ypres in 1915

111

before attacking the Canadian-held front line, Dr. Cluny McPherson hastily improvised a gas mask of metal and cloth. This was gradually improved to become the standard mask issued to all Allied soldiers. One of McPherson's crude early masks is still preserved in the Newfoundland Museum, on the top floor of the parliament building in St. John's.

Another protective device, but one which has had post-war values, is the anti-G suit, the invention of Dr. W. R. Franks. This is the ancestor of the pressure suit now playing such an important role in the conquest of outer space. Franks began work at the University of Toronto in the late Thirties and became, before the end of World War II, a leading authority on the effects of acceleration and decleration on the human body. His first G-suit had water pads tightly laced into the legs and was good for accelerations as high as seven or eight times the force of gravity. This enabled fighter pilots to remain conscious when their planes went into tight turns or steep dives.

To test Franks' G-suit, a human centrifuge had to be designed and constructed, the first in any Allied country. Built in Toronto in 1939, it consisted of a cockpit swung at the end of a rotating horizontal arm. The guinea-pig airman, racing around the circle 32 feet in diameter, experienced exactly the same sensations – blindness, followed by a complete blackout – that the fighter pilot felt in diving his Spitfire or forcing it into tight turns. Not only was this human centrifuge the basic research tool in developing the G-suit, but it was used in medical research programmes that

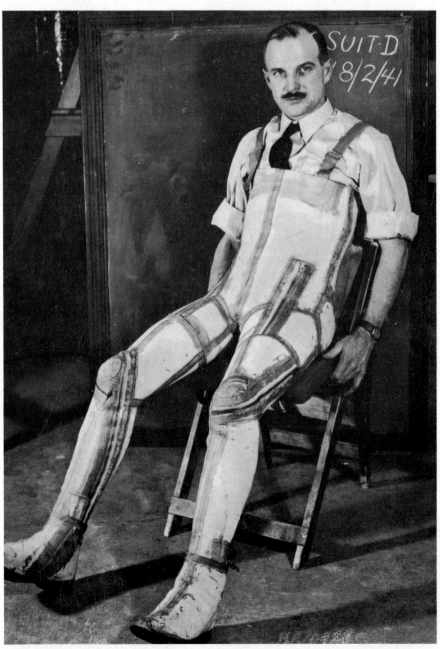

The need was critical: keep fighter pilots from blacking out in steep dives and sharp turns. Dr. W. R. Franks (above) *provided the solution in 1941 with his anti-G suit.*

taught a great deal about the reactions of the human body to flight.

The floating airfield

The most exotic research project carried out by Canadian teams in World War II was *Habakkuk*. This was the idea of producing a man-made iceberg with a flat top 2,000 feet long by 300 feet wide, and then anchoring it in the middle of the Atlantic Ocean so that it could serve as a staging stop for airplanes. It received its unusual name from a quotation from *Habakkuk* 1:5: "For I will work a work in your days which ye will not believe though it be told you."

The project first took shape in the fevered imagination of Geoffrey Pyke, an eccentric Englishman who convinced the commander of Command Operations, Lord Louis Mountbatten, who, in turn, convinced Prime Minister Winston Churchill. In 1942, such a landing stage was badly needed for ferrying new bombers and other types of aircraft from North America to England. Northern Canada was the ideal place to carry out research on *Habakkuk* and, in the autumn of 1942, research teams across the country were working on it.

Like most seemingly brand new ideas, even the scheme for a floating island in the middle of the Atlantic had predecessors. Frederick Creed, the Canadian inventor of the printing telegraph, had been working on his "seadrome," or floating station, for about 20 years. The 70-year-old Creed arrived at the need for mid-Atlantic stations through a problem connected with submarine telegraph cables. It

was well known that a telegraph's speed, and hence its capacity, could be quadrupled by the simple process of cutting it in half and inserting high-speed repeaters. Three such repeaters at equal intervals would multiply the speed of the transatlantic cable by 16.

In 1918 Creed designed a large floating station, solid enough to withstand North Atlantic gales, which was to be anchored half way across the ocean. Since the platform had to be very large to remain stable when waves 50 feet high and 500 feet long swept along it, the thought struck the inventor that such a platform could be used as a landing deck for trans-Atlantic aircraft. In the Thirties, these planes did not, of course, have the range of later models. The British Admiralty and Air Ministry looked into this proposal with the British airlines, but they came to the conclusion that the scheme was impracticable.

Creed didn't know about this decision and, in 1933, he came back to his original idea and made a carefully-thought-out design for a floating station that rested on partially submerged steel tubes. These tubes, when nearly filled with water, floated in a vertical position because of the air trapped in their top, on the same principle as a diving bell. Being over 100 feet long, the tubes were remarkably stable, since they rested on relatively calm water well below the motion of the highest wave. In its final form as developed by Creed in 1939, the seadrome was to be a tremendous structure – measuring 1,500 feet long and standing 50 feet above the water.

Havens in the Atlantic

Creed made careful studies of wave motion, and even worked out ingenious devices for studying the stresses caused by large waves. He argued, in a booklet published at his own expense, that his seadrome offered the British taxpayer a way to avoid the huge annual subsidy that the Government was giving the airlines: the aircraft business could pay its way by making relatively short hops.

Creed had a working model of his seadrome built on a scale of 1-to-150 and tested it in a swimming pool. Motion pictures of the test show the platform remaining completely stable as the equivalent of 100-foot waves swept along under it. This impressive demonstration was made in 1939 to the Institution of Engineers and Shipbuilders of Scotland.

Creed spent all the money he had earned over the years trying to get governments to listen to his plan for the floating station. In 1939, he saw clearly that the use of mobile airbases would ensure control of the North Atlantic sea lanes in wartime. He wrote: "If a line of seadromes were established at intervals of say, 350 miles, between the West of Ireland and the United States of America via Newfoundland, at a total cost of not more than $63,000,000, that would provide not only a safe and easy path for commercial and military planes in peacetime, but in time of war it would provide a safe lane 3,000 miles in length, 200 or 300 miles in breadth, which could be adequately patrolled and protected by planes and naval ships stationed on the seadromes. A lane into which

Frederick Creed made a fortune on his invention of the printing telegraph, but lost it all trying to promote his idea of "floating islands" for aircraft landings on the Atlantic.

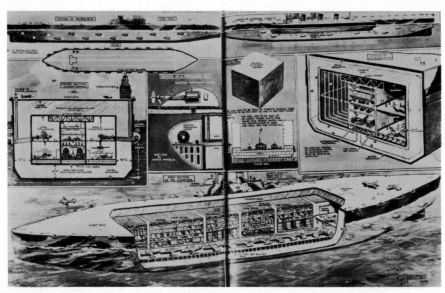

Cross-section diagrams of proposed floating airfields of ice, a top secret project in Canada during World War II until the Atlantic ferry system eliminated their need.

no hostile vessel could possibly penetrate and through which our vital supplies of food and material of every kind could be safely brought."† But the idea was unable to get even a hearing from anyone until Geoffrey Pyke added the notion of manufacturing the structure out of ice instead of steel, and pushed it through to Winston Churchill.

By the winter of 1942-43, several crash programmes were underway investigating the feasibility of the *Habakkuk* idea. At Patricia Lake, near Jasper, Alberta, and on Lake Louise, actual small-scale prototypes of ice islands were built. Pyke himself had suggested that since ice is really a viscous fluid, not a solid, some other ingredients should be added to strengthen the mix. Research proved that wood pulp, added in the proportion of 1-in-10 to the ice, made a composition that, weight for weight, was as strong as concrete, yet could be worked like wood. But, as research brought in more and more answers, it gradually became apparent that the floating ice island would not be inexpensive. It turned out that it would cost as much to build as an aircraft carrier of steel.

During 1942 the R.C.A.F. Ferry Command had developed a staging route by way of Gander, Greenland, and Iceland, which was working reasonably well. So *Habakkuk* came to an end, without a full-scale prototype ever having been built. And, before too long, the range of aircraft was extended so that the Atlantic became an easy hop.

†F. G. Creed, *The Seadrome or Floating Station*, Glasgow, 1939.

114

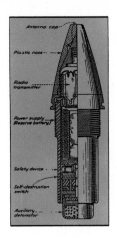

The proximity fuse, a product of Canadian, British and American cooperation, increased the killing power of anti-aircraft fire by an amazing 5,000 per cent.

Just a shack on an Alberta lake, but this was the site of Operation Habakkuk. *Behind those walls was one of the most closely-guarded secrets of the war* (see below).

These blocks of ice mixed with wood pulp were used in the Habakkuk *island experiment. Enthusiasm melted when the "islands" were priced as high as normal aircraft carriers.*

Two million a month

Second only to the atomic bomb, the most important weapon of World War II was the proximity fuse. As the speed of all vehicles, particularly aircraft, increased, it became very difficult to set a time fuse on a shell accurately enough to make it explode at the right moment. Chances of a direct hit on an aircraft were almost nil, and if the shell did not explode and scatter its shrapnel at just the right distance from a high-flying aircraft, no damage would be done. Early in the war it was estimated that it took 20,000 rounds of ammunition to shoot down one aircraft; after the development of the fuse, one aircraft was coming down for every 400 shells expended.

The development of the proximity fuse is one of the war's great stories of collaboration between Great Britain, the United States and Canada. In the middle Thirties, the increasing threat of German bombers caused English scientists to look carefully at any method of making anti-aircraft fire more accurate.

Very early in the war, the British produced a rocket, the *Harvey*, which allowed room in the nose-cone for some new types of fuses. The *Harvey* was very quickly fitted with a photoelectric type proximity fuse which determined for itself the right moment to explode, by judging changes in intensity of the light near an aircraft. This was the first crude predecessor of the modern device.

The problem was brought to Canada and the United States in 1940. At the University of Toronto, Arnold Pitt was put in charge of a crash

115

Arnold Pitt: a tiny, deadly fuse

John McLennan: low-temperature labs

programme. As it turned out, American scientists working on the project at the same time, worked more on the radar and electronic components of the fuse, while the Canadian share turned out to be the design and testing of the battery.

Pitt obtained R. W. McKay from the Ontario Research Foundation and, in due course, the research team came up with a radically new idea for providing power to the fuse. This was a tiny storage battery set into operation by the shock caused by firing the shell. A glass ampule broken by the shock allowed acid to flow over tiny battery plates which within half a second were producing power for the delicate radio transmitter and receiver crammed into the nose of the shell. As the shell approached its target, it sent out radar-like pulses which bounced back from the enemy and were recorded on its receiver. On reaching the correct distance from the target, the receiver circuits tripped a relay which fired the explosive.

All this was achieved in a shell head a little over an inch in diameter and two inches long, spinning rapidly, and closing with its target at a speed of 1,200 miles an hour. Mass production of the fuses in the United States eventually reached the rate of two million a month.

A difficult birth in plastics

The wartime project with the most lasting effect on the Canadian economy was probably the unglamorous manufacture of acetone from acetylene gas. In 1915 the British Ministry of War realized that its normal sources of supply of acetone for the manufacture of cordite (then the standard explosive) could never keep up with wartime needs. The Imperial Munitions Board in Ottawa had a German patent for the production of acetone from acetylene, which, however, had never been worked. They handed this over to H. W. Matheson, H. S. Reid, and A. F. G. Cadenhead, chemists at the works in Shawinigan Falls, Quebec. The process was long and complicated, and festooned with seemingly insuperable difficulties at every step, but, late in 1916, the first five tons of acetic acid was finally produced, and the following January saw shipment of the first carload of acetone. Gradually, out of this crash programme grew the substantial plastics industry we have in Canada today.

After World War I, the young chemists at Shawinigan went on to further fundamental research and took out basic patents on vinyls. During an attempt to make acetic anhidride, at that time imported from the United States, George Morrison noticed that small amounts of an unknown by-product were formed. On the advice of his boss, F. W. Skirrow, a five-gallon bottle of these by-products was set aside; a year later it was examined, and it was found to have polymerized into a transparent solid.

This was the first production of vinyl acetate in Canada. Working with K. G. Blaikie, the chemists worked out the basic patent coverage on polyvinyl alcohols, which are used today in coating fabrics and as molding compositions. A commonplace application is in the manufacture of safety glass.

Helium from Calgary

John McLennan, head of the physics department of the University of Toronto, seems to have spent World War I commuting to London, bothering the Board of Inventions and Research with suggestions. One of these was that the non-inflammable gas, helium, should be used as a substitute for the dangerous hydrogen in dirigibles. This was a good idea except that helium, because of its scarcity, was very expensive, selling for $7,000 a cubic foot.

Once he got the go-ahead signal, McLennan quickly assembled a research team of Toronto physicists who worked out means of extracting helium from natural gas. McLennan wheedled scarce equipment from England and made sure it was shipped to Calgary where there was an inexhaustible supply of natural gas. By the end of the war, mass production at Calgary had reduced the price of helium to 11 cents a cubic foot.

This wartime project had no direct effect on Canadian industry since the American production of helium from natural gas, begun in 1918, soon dwarfed the Canadian effort. But the project had an extremely important effect on the development of Canadian science and technology.

At the end of the war, Sir John – he had been knighted by King George V – persuaded the Admiralty to give him the supply of helium remaining in Canada, and also the equipment used to make it. With these, he set up the first low-temperature laboratory in Canada at the University of Toronto. The method used for separating helium from natural gas de-

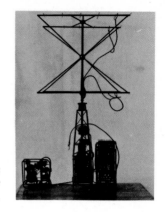

This radar device, manufactured by a Canadian Crown corporation, was used by the U.S. Army at Guadalcanal.

pended on liquefying all the other components of natural gas except helium, work which gave Canadian physicists and technicians practical experience in producing low temperatures with large-scale equipment.

With the assistance of Gordon Shrum, now Chancellor of Simon Fraser University, the first cryogenic laboratory in Canada was completed in 1923. Out of this came the Canadian work on superconductors (metals that lose their resistance to the flow of electricity at low temperatures) and other important projects.

Locating the enemy

Late in 1940, a group of Canadian businessmen gave the government gifts of more than one million dollars, to be used for any war purpose. This generous and far-seeing act made money available at once, without having to persuade committees or wait for appropriations. By a stroke of luck, the gift arrived just at the crucial moment when radar – the detection and ranging of objects by radio waves – was ready to make a great leap forward.

As far back as 1926, Major A. G. L. McNaughton and Colonel W. A. Steele had obtained a patent on a device which, with some extension of the meaning, might be called a radar. This was a method of using the cathode ray tube for radio direction finding. John Henderson, at the National Research Council during the Thirties, had been concerned with identifying and locating the thunder storms which caused radio static. By 1939, he was working on cathode ray direction-finding equipment small enough to be used on ships and aircraft.

For effective direction-finding by radar, however, there had to be a very narrow beam of radiation, and there were no tubes capable of giving high-power output at ultra-high frequencies. But, in 1940, a group of English physicists at the University of Birmingham developed the resonant-cavity magnetron. This tube was the key device which, for the first time, made radar practical.

In August and September 1940, Sir Henry Tizard headed a British scientific mission to Canada and the United States to demonstrate the first cavity magnetrons. The enthusiasm generated by the magnetron, and by members of the Tizard Mission who agreed to stay in Canada, was matched by the large timely gifts of money by Canadian businessmen. Within six months the National Research Council had a staff of two hundred engaged on radar, and Research Enterprises Ltd., a plant at Leaside, near Toronto, had an order for $30 millions' worth of radar gun-laying sets from the U.S. Government.

Research Enterprises, which had been planned as a small plant in Ottawa for assembling bits and pieces of optical equipment bought elsewhere, eventually employed 8,000 people. They made not only the gun-laying radar used in the defence of Britain, but also the mobile radar which the U.S. used for the invasion of Guadalcanal.

All during the middle years of the war, Americans used equipment that was basically British designed and Canadian built. Later in the war, when the huge American factories got into production, radar sets were produced like eggs. But in the early days it was a case of using Canadian-built radars, or nothing.

Pin-pointing the raider

There were at least two Canadian inventive contributions to world radar. At McGill University, a group under Professor W. H. Watson, and including Professor Ernest Guptil (who still holds basic patents), produced the slotted waveguide. This is an efficient method of taking energy from transmitter to antenna.

Although there is room for argument, it seems probable too that the so-called "magnetic" sweep used in radar display systems is a Canadian invention. The plan-position indicator is the device which locates an enemy aircraft horizontally on the map. This P.P.I. is a large cathode-ray tube in which the sweep moves around like the second hand of a clock. The sweep was made to rotate, in the early sets, by means of a yoke on the neck of the tube which generated a magnetic field. This yoke was made to rotate by means of an electric motor, that is, by mechanical means. A group at the N.R.C. including Harold McRae, Ross Smyth and Bill Haney, were the first to use an electrically rotating field, making use of a Selsyn on the cathode ray tube itself. The substitution of electrical for mechanical methods represented an important advance in radar not only because of the precision with which the beam could be rotated, but also because it eliminated many operating and maintenance difficulties.

10 / MISCELLANY
Imagination and ingenuity

Sir Alan Herbert, the English humorist and member of parliament, advocates a scheme for rewarding authors by paying them a small royalty each time their books are taken out of a public library. If this were done for inventors – who are kicked around by society even more than authors – and we had to deposit a penny each time we used the brainchild of a fellow Canadian, we would be amazed how many times each day we would have to pay. In time, we would be amazed, too, at the flood of new and valuable inventions changing our lives, because when men get paid for their work, they start working twice as hard. Whenever we use an electrical appliance like a toaster, or redecorate a room, or zip up a zipper, or go skating, or watch a horse race, or carry home some beer, we unconsciously pay tribute to the labours of a forgotten or little known Canadian inventor.

Toward the end of the 19th century, Canada's best-known product in other parts of the world was probably the humble ice skate. John Forbes, of Halifax, had invented his spring skate as far back as 1854 and, by 1861, the Star Manufacturing Company, of Dartmouth, Nova Scotia, had been set up to make it. A few years later, James Whelpley invented the "long reacher" ice skate especially for use on the long reaches of smooth ice found on the New Brunswick rivers. This is very similar to what we call a racing skate today, except that it was fastened to ordinary shoes with a pair of straps, rather than rivetted to skating boots. Long reachers were sold in many parts of the world, and developed into an export industry quite large for the time.

For the "sport of kings", Canadians seem to have concentrated on ensuring fair starts. Philip McGinnis, of Huntingdon, Quebec, went to New York where he became a reporter for the New York *Sun*. His beat was the race tracks. In those days the prevailing system of throwing down a red flag to start horse races led to endless disputes and many unfair starts. August Belmont, head of the New York Jockey Club, felt that science should be able to produce something better, and encouraged McGinnis to think about it. Eventually, the Canadian built a prototype starting barrier in a small machine shop in Brooklyn. It was an instant success.

McGinnis gave up the newspaper business, returned to Canada and began manufacturing his "gate" at London. It was essentially strands of wire lowered across the track in a spring levered device; the barrier flew

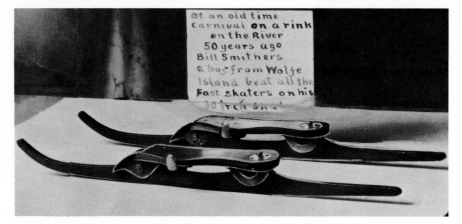

Giant strides: these 30-inch "long reachers" wore a made-in-Canada label, mid-19th century.

up at the starter's touch. Although he lacked engineering training, Mc-Ginnis produced his own drawings and designs, made his own patterns and then had castings made in Owen Sound. When orders came with a rush, the McGinnis children were put to work assembling the gate. Patented in the U.S., Canada and several foreign countries, it produced a substantial income for many years.

Eventually, the McGinnis equipment was superseded and replaced by the electrically operated stall-type starting gate, also a Canadian development.

Speed queens of the lakes

The residents of the district around London, Ontario, have always had a particular interest in high speed on water. Larry Wilson, later president of the Ingersoll Machine Tool Company, built the *Miss Canada* series of racing hydroplanes there. First, his craft were in the 225-cubic-inch class; then his larger boats won the North American championships all during the 1930s. Guy Lombardo, a London boy then just beginning his climb to fame as an orchestra leader, also fell in love with the racing hydroplanes. Profits from his highly successful *Royal Canadians* were put into a series of boats called *Miss Tempo* which, with Lombardo as driver, dominated competition in North America for several years.

The highest development of the racing hydroplane came with the series of *Miss Supertest* boats built by J. Gordon Thompson, president of Supertest Petroleum Corporation, of London, and driven by Bob Hayward.

He was a world-famous bandleader, but this boy-who-made-good from London, Ontario, was also well known as a speedboat king. His name was Guy Lombardo, and in 1946 he won the National Sweepstakes and the International Gold Cup.

Before 1959, Canada had never won a Harmsworth Trophy . . . but then came Miss Supertest III. *Built by Jim Thompson, driven by Bob Hayward, she took the trophy three years in a row. Hayward's death ended her career.*

119

Steve Pasjack and his tuck-away handle: it made beer cartons easy to carry for the buyers, simple to store for the brewers.

These boats practically took the Harmsworth Trophy out of competition, winning it for Canada three times in a row. *Miss Supertest III*, driven by a reworked Rolls-Royce Griffon engine, and with much redesigning of the gearbox and propellers, reached 160 miles an hour on the straightaways. Designed in 1958, she raced only four times, but there wasn't a craft that could beat her. Driver Bob Hayward was killed on September 10, 1961, in a racing accident, and Thompson withdrew his boats from competition. The championship *Miss Supertest III* has since been donated to the Ontario Centre for Science and Technology.

This was one of the later models of Wanzer's lamp, dating about 1880s.

AROUND THE HOUSE

Among the many inventors who have contributed to our standard of living – reputedly second only to that of the United States – must be listed an immigrant from Pennsylvania named R. M. Wanzer. He came to Hamilton, Ontario, in 1860 and produced the Wanzer lamp, which gave a flame sufficiently powerful to be used for cooking as well as lighting. His lamp was unique, partly because it had no chimney, but chiefly because there was a clock mechanism in the base which drove a small fan. This produced an artificial forced draft and therefore a brighter burning wick. On some versions the wick was said to be adjusted automatically for length (that is, self trimmed as it burned) by being linked to the same clock mechanism in the base. The only example of the clockwork Wanzer lamp I have seen is preserved in the museum at Dundas, Ontario. There is a later model in the Patent Office in Ottawa, dated 1885, but by this time the lamp had reverted to the conventional form.

Wanzer seems also to have manufactured in 1861 the first sewing machine made in Canada. At one time, sewing machines were being made at the rate of 1,000 a week, but Wanzer later ran into money troubles and his company sank under the surface of the corporate ocean, leaving no trace.

A name still on sewing machines today is that of Charles Raymond. Already a skilled mechanic in 1863 when he arrived in Canada, Raymond registered a long string of patents from his factory at Brantford, Ont.

"Do-it-yourself" era

The paint roller is a good example of a very simple Canadian invention that has ushered in a change in our way of living. Invented and patented by Norman Breakey, of Toronto, in 1940, it revolutionized the painting and decorating industry, and did much to introduce the era of do-it-yourself home decorating. The inventor did not make money from it, chiefly because he had no capital to fight patent infringers and was never able to persuade people to risk money backing him.

One of the most ubiquitous of mechanical inventions is the zipper. Dr. Gideon Sundback is believed by some authorities to be entitled to the credit of inventing the zipper, in the form that we know today. Chief engineer of the Lightning Fastener Company, at St. Catharines, Ontario, in the 1940s, he not only redesigned the old slide fastener to make the modern zipper, but also invented a series of machines for zipper manufacture. These now provide about 75 per cent of world production. The first man to dream up the idea of the zipper was the American W. L. Judson; he obtained his patents in 1891 and 1893, but he never succeeded in selling the idea.

The disappearing handle

The beer carton with the tucked-in handle is the brainchild of Steve Pasjack, of Vancouver. Like many of us, he used to wonder why he had to carry an awkward case of beer under his arm but, unlike the rest of us, Pasjack set out to do something about

Morse Robb was 24 when he invented his wave organ, with the help of a local church organ. His was the fore-runner of all the home electric organs of today.

it. He was in the corrugated carton business, and a package designer by trade. In short order, he came up with the carton we have today; the handle disappears so that the cases can be stacked evenly but pops up for easy carrying.

A mild, soft-spoken man, Pasjack is embarrassed by rumours that his invention made him a millionaire. Actually, he was in no position to build a patent fence and had to be satisfied with a modest return.

Making water purer

One of the most remarkable inventors ever to make a living in Canada was Frank G. Negus, of Nova Scotia. Although completely innocent of formal education, he was ingenious enough to make a fair living out of his forty odd inventions – some of them very odd. These ranged from a brake for railroad trains, through electrical equipment, to chlorine cells for water purification. He seems like a character from another era but he died only in 1964.

People who worked with Negus remember a very jolly, well-rounded fellow who was half inventor, half promoter. He bore a disconcerting resemblance to the comedian W. C. Fields. One story about Negus is that when he was trying to sell local authorities on one of his inventions – a detector for chlorine in water – he put in a little *Javex* bleach when the authorities weren't looking, just to make sure that his chlorine cell had something to work on.

Negus claimed in the Thirties the invention of a cell for producing chlorine from sea water. This had

actually been invented long before, but Negus' ingenuity made up for his lack of originality, and he produced a very efficient piece of water-processing equipment.

Charles H. Castell, who knew Negus and who is now at the Atlantic Fisheries Experimental Station, in Halifax, writes: "He was a very ingenious man and a first-class mechanic. I sincerely believe that if he had had scientific backing to show him the clear picture of the use and limitations of his equipment, he might well have changed the treatment of water in many parts of Canada... Most of the health authorities ignored or laughed at him, and his financial backers were too ignorant to see that his greatest need was accurate measurements made by recognized scientists. In recent years his ideas have been taken over by enterprising American firms, and have been tested by various u.s. authorities. They are now being used quite extensively across the border."

CHANSON TRISTE ON THE ROBB ORGAN

Every year, the Minister of Finance in Ottawa announces that the Government is worried about Canada's adverse balance of trade. In a normal year, we buy abroad about $500 million in goods more than we are able to sell. The money must come from somewhere, so what happens is that the Canadian dollar begins to sell at a discount in world markets and everything we buy abroad costs more. In the history of Canadian invention we have had – and wasted – several glorious opportunities to correct our

adverse balance of trade. If we had been alert to innovation, and if the inventors had been able to get enough support, several brilliant ideas could have developed into major export industries.

One of the most fascinating of these opportunities concerns the electronic wave organ, invented by Morse Robb, of Belleville, Ontario, in 1927. In the United States alone, $300 million worth of electronic organs were sold in a recent year. If we had seized our opportunity to become the world's supplier of electronic organs (the way the Swiss, for instance, have become world suppliers of watches) this one item alone would be enough most years to reverse our international trade position and give us a favourable balance.

The conventional organ dates from the 5th century. It produces musical tones through the vibration of columns of air in long pipes. But an organ is a very expensive instrument, and even in large churches it is sometimes difficult to find space for the bank of pipes required. Robb set out to bring the mighty music of the organ into the home.

A thin intense man with a shock of blond hair, he got his basic idea for the wave organ in 1926, when he was only 24. His idea was to record the wave form of the actual sound produced by an organ pipe and then work out means of picking up the tone again from the permanent recording.

Of course, he was not the only one working in this field in the Twenties. With the development of radio broadcasting, many people were trying to make musical tones by artificial means. The commonest method was

to set up an oscillator which would produce a series of tones electronically. All these attempts and methods finally culminated in the familiar electronic organ as manufactured by the Hammond, Baldwin and Conn companies. The Robb wave organ was the first instrument of this new generation. It was not only first in conception by about eight years, but it was the first to be patented in Canada, the United States and England, and was the first to be manufactured and released for public sale.

The United Church Sound

Robb got his head start on his contemporaries by sticking stubbornly to one basic principle instead of allowing himself to go with the crowd. As radio techniques became more sophisticated and radio-tube technology developed in the Thirties, most experimenters with electric organs allowed themselves to be seduced by the idea of making sounds by pure electronic means in an oscillator. This was attractive because of its simplicity, compactness, and cheapness, but the technique had flaws.

Morse Robb got his basic wave forms naturally by recording the individual notes of the organ at the Bridge Street United Church in Belleville. The organist, Leo Riggs, let Robb take a pipe right out of the church and blow it to obtain his oscillograph picture. Robb photographed the wave forms as they appeared on the oscillograph, using a special camera he had built, and from the resulting photographs he was able to trace exact wave form pictures of each of the notes. From these tracings

the wave forms were then cut into the outer surface of a steel drum. When this drum was made to revolve under an electro-magnetic pick-up head, it produced a series of electric impulses which could be put through an amplifier and reproduced as a single sound.

Musicians have always hated any instrument that attempted to produce musical tones by artificial means. Even today, most people with musical training still dislike the Hammond-type organs; with the crude instruments available in the Thirties, they had good reason.

Robb saw immediately his first job was to convince important musicians that his new principle was different and that his wave organ was an instrument musicians could respect. In 1927 he demonstrated his organ in Toronto to musicians, music critics and journalists. This resulted in Canadian executives of the General Electric Company arranging a demonstration at the G.E.C. Laboratories, in Schenectady, New York, where even the chairman of the board listened and was impressed. These were the first public demonstrations of electronic organ tones in North America, and probably in the world.

Trying to find capital

As a result of the favourable reaction from musicians, and of acclaim in the newspapers, Robb was prepared to make a deal in 1927 either with General Electric or another company for manufacturing the instrument. But, on the advice of his father, who was then a vice-president of Canadian National Railways, and the concur-

ring opinion of the multi-millionaire W. H. Miner, the Canadian inventor of the Miner gear for coupling railways cars, young Robb decided to find his own development money and set up in the manufacturing business himself. With the benefit of hindsight, this was a mistake. Inventing and manufacturing are quite different and it is usually better for the inventor to allow an experienced manufacturer and distributor to get his product to the public.

For the next year Robb worked on improving his invention and getting it patented. The Canadian patent was issued under No. 284183 on October 23, 1928, and the U.S. patent No. 1785915 was granted on December 23, 1930. Now, the usual money troubles began to appear: Robb's father, for example, began to have second thoughts when he saw the bills flooding in from the patent attorneys.

In a letter to his father about this time, Morse Robb shows the inventor's complete faith in his brainchild and demonstrates a very clear conception of what is involved in making an invention:

"I hope no one has any idea that there is a possibility that it might really not be wise to spend the money for development on account of something that might be disclosed when the patent search is completed . . . It will startle the musical world and be acclaimed the greatest instrument of all and the world will not let it stagnate. It will be manufactured at once regardless of whether or not it is completely protected by patents, and in one way or another it will pay the creators. If inventors allowed themselves to become scared by Patent Office disclosures,

Though his organ was not a commercial success, Robb still works on inventions, using a corner of a living room in his Belleville, Ontario, home as a workshop.

practical progress in inventing would come to a standstill. There were telephone patents before Bell, electric light patents and phonograph patents before Edison, and wireless patents by the score before Marconi."

In 1929 the stock market collapsed and people who had money available to encourage new technology either lost it or suddenly became very cautious. Constantly hampered by lack of funds, Robb tried to improve his demonstrations and make some arrangements for manufacturing. In 1931, he made an agreement with the famous firm of Casavant Frères, of St. Hyacinthe, Quebec, but that company itself was short of money in the Depression and the agreement was allowed to lapse.

In 1932 Robb got the cultivated ear of H. Napier Moore, then editor of *Maclean's* magazine. Moore telephoned his friend, Sir Ernest MacMillan, conductor of the Toronto Symphony Orchestra and, even more important, an organist of world class. MacMillan listened and was impressed. He, in turn, got the wealthy Lady Eaton to meet the inventor and hear his story. Between 1932 and 1935, Robb had considerable correspondence with Lady Eaton's secretary.

Finally, enough money was obtained from several sources to enable Robb to begin manufacturing the organ himself. The Robb Wave Organ Company was set up at Belleville and, early in 1936, the first organs were delivered to stores and chapels in the Toronto area. One was installed in the dining room of the main Eaton department store.

The next year a wave organ was installed at the Canadian National Exhibition, and many public demonstrations took place. Full-page advertisements appeared in the Toronto papers, offering the Robb organ in the large console size at $2,600 and a smaller portable model at under $2,000.

There is no doubt in my mind that, even as late as 1937, the Robb organ was superior to the Hammond and its other American rivals. However, it failed completely as a commercial enterprise. As is usually the case in the story of a complex invention, there is no single cause for failure.

It is easy to see now that the promoters and the inventor made a mistake in not taking their patent immediately upon issue to the largest u.s. manufacturer of organs. Patents almost always lead to a fight, and if you're going to be in a fight it is important to have well-muscled friends. On the other hand, it is easy to see why Robb recoiled from the idea of working with a large corporation. Inventors are individualists who look at problems in unconventional ways. They do not work well in harness – particularly in harness with conventional thinkers of the type who often make a success of a manufacturing business.

A second reason for the failure of the Robb organ was the Depression itself. Music is a luxury, and musical instruments selling at between $2,000 and $3,000 clearly did not find much acceptance at a time when first mortgages were being abandoned and owners were giving up millions of dollars' worth of real estate by "quit claim" deeds.

Again, there must have been imperfections in the wave organ itself.

No new instrument ever starts out with perfect tone. A Toronto organist, Harvey Robb (no relation to the inventor), wrote in 1937:

"While in some respects the organ was very successful, in others it fell down badly. The chief fault was in its lack of dependability. There seems to be a lack of experienced workmanship in the assembling of the instrument. An instrument that will work one time and not the next, is of no use. . ."

The first examples of a new product on the market are always imperfect to some degree. When the first successful locomotive made its first run in 1804, all the respectable business men of the community laughed because its entire payload consisted of coal, which was used up by the time the locomotive reached its destination! The engine clearly had no economic utility. But, within ten years, locomotives were carrying fifty times their own weight and, thirty years later, they carried not only enough coal for long journeys but towed trains of box cars carrying more than one hundred times the locomotive's weight.

The final reason for the failure of the Robb organ must be that the inventor himself finally became discouraged. All societies have a built-in resistance to innovation. The main task of the inventor, once he has succeeded in thinking of something new, is to work out ways and means of convincing society that he should be listened to. This often is a long and highly discouraging task. Young men of 25 are not usually philosophical enough, or experienced enough in the ways of the world, to carry such a difficult task to a conclusion.

F. A. Knapp tested his "roller boat" in Toronto, 1897. It proved too slow to turn over a profit.

EVER HEARD OF THE MECHANICAL HAT LIFTER?
daffy deVices
IT'S ONLY ONE OF HUNDREDS OF FAR-OUT NOTIONS PATENTED IN CANADA

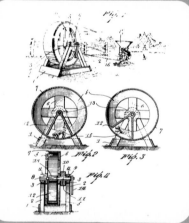

Pet power: this "motor" patented in the 1920s would allow every family dog to earn its keep.

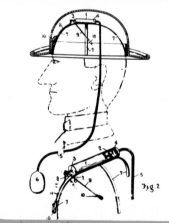

Automated manners: with this 1912 item, a gent could tip his hat without getting cold hands.

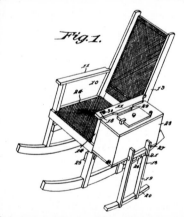

No loafing with Moses Cardin's rocking chair of 1922: it churned butter while you rocked.

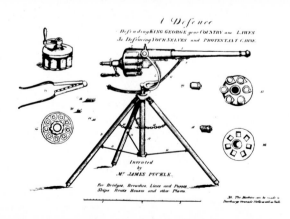

James Puckle devised this wacky weapon 200 years ago, recommending round bullets for shooting Christians, square ones for shooting Turks.

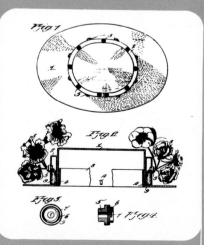

A water reservoir on this 1908 bonnet kept flowers from wilting.

EPILOGUE
The need to take risks

There is no necessary limit to the extent to which inventive genius may benefit mankind. The way to bring this about is to increase the demand, that is, to increase the capacity of society for receiving and appreciating these new benefits. It is not the inventor who needs educating, but the user of his invention, *i.e.* the general public.‡

For the past fifty years the politicians and the pundits have been asserting that "the 20th century belongs to Canada." We are, at this writing, two-thirds of the way through the 20th century, and Canada gives no signs of owning it. On the contrary, since the beginning of the century our industrial strength has declined when compared to that of several European nations, and particularly when compared to Japan's.

For a country uniquely rich in raw materials, possessing a diligent work force and a stable government, Canada has made remarkably slow progress over the past 100 years. I am well aware this is not the generally accepted view – but it is true, nevertheless. The most important question facing Canada today is not bilingualism, nor is it cultural growth: it is the problem of economic backwardness which leaves us increasingly weak in competition with other nations.

There are many reasons for our debility. First of all, one-third of all Canadians, until very recently, had hardly been touched by universal education. English-speaking Canadians had modern schools, mechanics' institutes, and colleges a century ago. In education, Quebec is still trying to fight its way into the 19th century.

Another basic weakness lies in the Canadian geography. In atomic power, energy is not released until a system reaches the packed condition known as "critical mass"; social energies can not be fully released in Canada because our twenty million people are spread thin along a ribbon of land 30 miles wide by 3,000 miles long. If our population were all jammed into a smaller area, the sharpest minds would clash frequently and, as steel sharpens steel, put a cutting edge on the national intellect. There would be more communication between leaders and thinkers – in short, the normal intellectual life of a Western society. But since Canadians are separated physically by vast distances, and since we have no viable journals of ideas, every Canadian idea-man or innovator tends to think he is completely alone.

But the main reason for Canada's slug-like growth is that our really good ideas have to be taken abroad for development. In the mass, we are a timid people, afraid of ourselves and terrified by the demands of the real world. In every area of human activity – art, business, literature, education – we have been content to let others take the risk of presenting new ideas. Canadians have too often been afraid to perform what George Leonard calls "the most outrageous and bewildering of human acts . . . saying the simple obvious truth before people are willing to hear it."

It is perfectly natural to be afraid of anything new. In the old days, before science began to affect every shade and shape of our existence, this fear of innovation didn't cost much. But today things are different. With the world recasting itself at ever-increasing speed, out-dated conservative attitudes can impoverish us by taking away our jobs. Moreover, individuals must overcome the fear of new ideas if they are to achieve their full potential. A crazy idea like harnessing electricity, laughed at by all respectable people in the 1880s, has become the means for all of us to enjoy a longer and easier life. What would your grandfather have said to an inventor's enthusiastic description of colour television?

I repeat that Canadians have made contributions to world science and technology out of all proportion to their small numbers. Some Canadian inventions made major world industries possible, but we have so often ended up importing from England, Belgium, Italy, the United States, billions of dollars' worth of equipment invented here. Unless this problem is corrected, it will leave us unable to compete as a major industrial nation in the modern world.

‡L. F. Ward, *The Psychic Factors of Civilization*, London, 1892.

INDEX

PICTURE CREDITS

Order of appearance in the text of pictures listed here is left to right, top to bottom. After the first recording, principal sources are credited under these abbreviations: The A. G. Bell Museum, Baddeck, N.S., AGBM; The Bell Telephone Historical Collection, BTHC; J.J. Brown Collection, JJBC; *Canada's Flying Heritage* by Ellis, CFH; DeHavilland photograph, DH; Eldorado Mining and Refining Limited, EMRL; Imperial Oil Limited, IOL; Miller Services, MS; National Research Council, NRC; Ontario Hydro, OH; John Ross Robertson Collection, JRRC; Toronto Public Library, TPL; Toronto Star Syndicate, TSS. Cover by Dennis Colwell / 9 *The Canadian Magazine* / 10 Northern Electric Co. Ltd. / 11 Bell Telephone Historical Collection; Bettmann Archive; BTHC / 12 Photograph by Gilbert H. Grosvenor © National Geographic Society / 13 Photograph by David G. McCurdy © the Bell Family and the National Geographic Society; Culver Pictures; Canada's Flying Heritage by Ellis; RCAF photograph / 14 A. G. Bell Museum, Baddeck, N.S., AGBM; J. J. Brown Collection / 15 AGBM; AGBM; AGBM; AGBM; Bell Family © National Geographic Society / 17 JJBC / 18 Courtesy of the Molson Archives, Molson Breweries Limited / 19 *Early American Steamers*, Toronto Public Library; "Canada's Royal William" by J. D. Kelly, Confederation Life Collection / 20 John Ross Robertson Collection, TPL; JRRC, TPL / 21 JRRC, TPL / 22 BTHC / 23 Photo by Gilbert H. Grosvenor © National Geographical Society; DeHavilland photograph / 24 Miller Services / 25 JRRC, TPL; Canadian Pacific photograph / 27 Sicard Inc.; Ontario Department of Tourism and Information / 28 Canadair Limited; Jiger Corporation Limited; JJBC / 29 Canadair Limited; JJBC; Sicard, Inc. / 31 CFH / 32 CFH / 32-33 Bettmann Archive / 34 Courtesy of Mr. G. Deland; DH; DH / 35 DH; DH / 36 The New York *Times* / 37 Orenda Graphics; Toronto Daily *Star* / 38 Avro Aircraft photograph; Orenda Graphics / 39 Toronto Star Syndicate / 40 *The Engineering Journal*, February, 1959; National Research Council / 41 NRC; NRC / 43 MS; MS; George T. Taylor photograph in the Lord Beaverbrook Collection / 44 Public Archives of Canada / 45 NRC / 46 *New Brunswick Courier* / 47 JRRC, TPL; Ontario Hydro; OH; / 48 OH; OH / 49 OH; OH; OH / 50 OH / 51 OH; *Compressed Air Magazine* / 52 OH; OH; *The Electrical News*, OH; Ottawa Transportation Commission/53 OH; OH / 54 Winnipeg *Free Press*; TSS / 55 Eldorado Mining and Refining Limited; EMRL / 56 EMRL; EMRL / 57 TTS / 59 MS / 60 The London (Ontario) *Free Press*, 1859 / 61 *The Scientific American*; *Commercial Directory for Hamilton* 1862, Imperial Oil Limited; *Commercial Directory for Hamilton* 1862, IOL / 63 The Oil Museum of Canada; Ontario Department of Tourism and Information; IOL; IOL; IOL / 65 IOL; IOL / 66 IOL; JJBC / 68 *Pulp and Paper Magazine of Canada* / 69 *Canadian Illustrated News*, TPL / 70 *Canadian Scenery*, TPL / 85 JJBC; BTHC / 86 JJBC; BTHC; BTHC; BTHC / 87 JJBC; JRRC, TPL / 88 Creed and Company Limited; *Canadian Illustrated News*, TPL / 89 *Canadian Illustrated News*, TPL / 90 Bettmann Archive / 91 *The Quiet Canadian* by Sir Wm. Stephenson / 93 Edward Samuel Rogers Memorial Collection / 95 *Fortune* Magazine, November, 1946 / 97 International Business Machines / 98 Photograph by Don Newlands / 99 TSS / 100 CAE Industries Limited; JJBC / 101 University of Toronto / 102 Crown Copyright, Science Museum, London, England / 103 JJBC; MS; MS / 104-105 JJBC / 106 MS; MS; MS / 107 Canada Department of Agriculture / 108 Canada Department of Agriculture; photograph by Harold Whyte / 109 Drake Family Collection; photograph by Harold Whyte / 111 Royal Canadian Military Institute / 112 Institute of Aviation Medicine / 114 JJBC; *Illustrated London News*, TPL; / 115 NRC; NRC; NRC / 117 NRC / 118 Courtesy of Mr. P. J. McGinnis / 119 *Canadian Illustrated News*, TPL; TSS; TSS; Supertest Petroleum / 120 Photograph by Selwyn Pullan; Hamilton *Spectator* / 121 Toronto Daily *Star* / 122 JJBC; photograph by Don Newlands / 124 JRRC, TPL; TSS; TSS; *The Canadian* Magazine; TSS; TSS.

The type-faces chosen for this book are Melior and Waverley, set in Canada by Cooper & Beatty, Limited and LinoComp. The book was printed and bound in Italy by Arnoldo Mondadori, Officine Grafiche. Text for picture albums in this book was written by Walt McDayter.